IN A TASSILI RAVINE, CYPRESSES PROVIDE EVIDENCE OF A MILDER PAST

A HAZY DUSK FALLS OVER BILMA OASIS

PEA-SIZED PEBBLES ON THE SURFACE OF A GRAVEL PLAIN

SAND WASHED DOWN FROM THE TASSILI MOUNTAINS

LIFE NATURE LIBRARY
LIFE SCIENCE LIBRARY
GREAT AGES OF MAN
FOODS OF THE WORLD
TIME-LIFE LIBRARY OF ART
LIFE LIBRARY OF PHOTOGRAPHY
THE EMERGENCE OF MAN
THE OLD WEST
THE ART OF SEWING
THE GREAT CITIES

THE SAHARA

THE WORLD'S WILD PLACES/TIME-LIFE BOOKS/AMSTERDAM

BY JEREMY SWIFT
AND THE EDITORS OF TIME-LIFE BOOKS

WITH PHOTOGRAPHS BY PIERRE BOULAT

Editorial Staff for *The Sahara*:
EDITOR: John Man
Deputy Editor: Simon Rigge
Picture Editor: Pamela Marke
Design Consultant: Louis Klein
Staff Writers:
Mike Brown, Mally Cox, Kate Dorment,
Dan Freeman, Heather Sherlock,
Timberlake Wertenbaker
Art Director: Graham Davis
Design Assistant: Joyce Mason
Picture Researchers:
Susan Stratton, Karin Pearce
Picture Assistant: Angela McNeill
Editorial Co-ordinator: Jackie Matthews

Consultants
Botany: Christopher Grey-Wilson, Phyllis Edwards
Geology: Dr. Peter Stubbs
Herpetology: David Ball
Ichthyology: Dr. Alwyne Wheeler
Invertebrates: Dr. Michael Tweedie
Ornithology: I. J. Ferguson-Lees
Zoology: Dr. P. J. K. Burton

Valuable assistance was given in the
preparation of this volume by the following
Time-Life correspondents: Maria Vincenza
Aloisi, Paris; Liz Kraemer, Bonn; Ann
Natanson, Rome.

Published by Time-Life International (Nederland) B.V.
5, Ottho Heldringstraat, Amsterdam 1018

The Author: Jeremy Swift, a Research Fellow at the University of Sussex, has done extensive field research in the Sahara, living with Tuareg herdsmen. He is trained as a biologist and an economist, and has published scientific papers on bird behaviour, natural parks and nomadism as well as a book on the environmental crisis called *The Other Eden—A New Approach to Man, Nature and Society*. He is Chairman of the Anti-Slavery and Aborigines Protection Societies.

Special Consultants: John Cloudsley-Thompson has written numerous books on desert ecology. He was Professor of Zoology at the University of Khartoum and Keeper of the Sudan Natural History Museum for 11 years. He is currently Professor of Zoology at Birkbeck College, University of London.

Andrew Warren is a specialist in desert morphology. He has travelled in Saharan Libya, Algeria and Niger and is co-author of the book, *Geomorphology in Deserts*. He teaches geography and conservation at University College London.

The Cover: Intense light and shadow create a surreal effect on the curved faces of a Saharan sand dune. The precise, almost geometric, proportions of many of the desert's sand-forms, which occupy only a fraction of its total area, are the result of the modelling action of the winds.

Contents

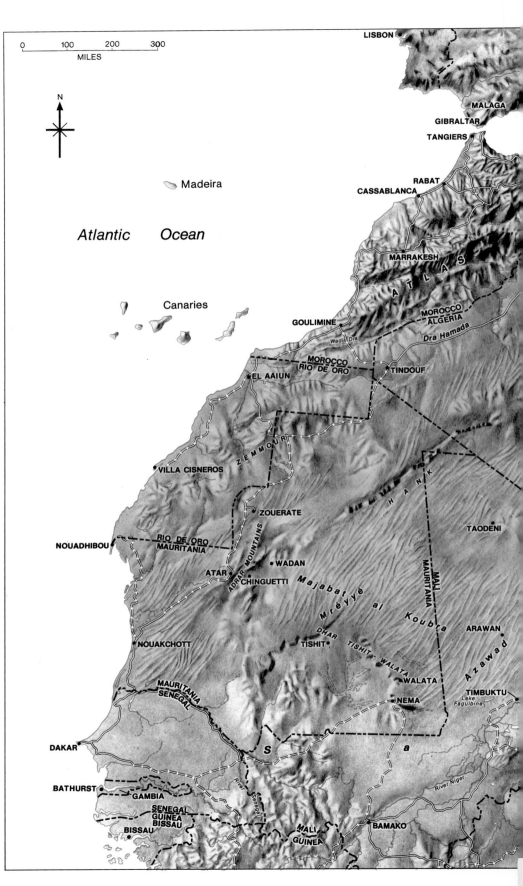

A World of Rock, Gravel and Sand

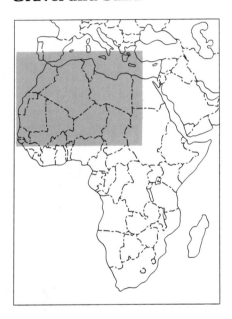

The Sahara blankets almost the entire
northern third of Africa. The area
covered in this book (brown rectangle
above) is mostly rock and gravel
(dark brown shading right). In the centre,
with extensions to the south and east,
rises the desert's mountain spine (light
brown shading). Surrounding the
mountains are vast gravel plains or reg
—the detritus of ancient rivers that, in
the Sahara's less arid past, flowed from
the mountains. In the north, the reg are
broken up by flat-topped plateaux, or
hamadas, whose surfaces are strewn
with coarse stones. The remainder is
sand (shaded yellow), swept across the
reg by the wind into sand seas or ergs
which, contrary to the popular view,
form only a quarter of the desert. Five
main tracks take direct north-south
routes across the Sahara. Broken blue
lines trace dried up river beds that
flood after the occasional rains.

Balearics
Sardinia
ATHENS

GRANADA
Sicily

ALGIERS
TUNIS
Malta
Crete

ORAN

Mediterranean Sea

BISKRA
TRIPOLI
BENGHAZI

M O U N T A I N S
LAGHOUAT

SAHARAN ATLAS
GHARDAÏA
EL OUED
TOUGGOURT

BECHAR
SIWA

WARGLA
EL GOLEA

Wadi Saoura
Great Western Erg
Great Eastern Erg
TUNISIA ALGERIA
GHADAMES
Hamada el Homra
Calansho Serir

Hamada

Tademaït Hamada
Tinrhert Hamada
Idehan Ubari
SEBHA

Erg Chech
Touat
AIN SALAH
Libyan Desert
KUFRA

Tidikelt
Fadnoun Plateau

EGYPT LIBYA

TASSILI N AJJER
Tihodaine Erg
Tiherir
MOUNTAINS
GHAT
Idehan Murzuq

AHNET
MOUIDIR
DJANET

Adrar Erg
AHAGGAR MOUNTAINS
Assekrem
Tahat
ATAKOR
TAMANRASSET
Adrar Erg
Wadi Tafassasset
DJADO PLATEAU
LIBYA CHAD

ALGERIA MALI
SILET
TIBESTI MOUNTAINS

Wadi Tamanrasset
ALGERIA NIGER
Emi Koussi
Wanyanga Serir

Tanezrouft
Timmissao Well
T é n é r é

ADRAR N IFORAS
Adrar Bous
FAYA
ENNEDI MOUNTAINS

Greboun

Wadi Tilemsi
AIR MOUNTAINS
BILMA
Bilma Erg

Wadi Azaouak
CHAD SUDAN

GAO
AGADES

h
e
IN GALL
I

MALI NIGER

MALI UPPER VOLTA
ZINDER
NIGER NIGERIA

River Niger
NIAMEY
Lake Chad

WAGADOUGOU
N'JAMENA

NIGERIA CAMEROUN

DAHOMEY

1/ Greatest of Deserts

Africa is divided into four parts. . . . The third part has no other name in Arabic but Sahra, which means desert.

LEO AFRICANUS/ 1550

From the Atlantic coast of Africa, the Sahara stretches, three thousand miles wide and a thousand deep, east to the Red Sea. This huge desert is a mysterious and unfinished place, a trial run in landscape architecture where a few basic designs of sand, gravel and mountains are used repeatedly and stretched to their limits. The mountains are uncompromisingly severe; the sand dunes have a regularity unknown elsewhere in nature; the gravel plains are oceanic in scale, flat and unchanging for days of travel. In the open desert there is too much sky, oppressively stretching from horizon to flat horizon, while in the sandstone canyons there is almost none at all.

To some eyes such a landscape would be monotonous. But to me these simple uncluttered lines have a purity lacking in more conventionally beautiful places. Here, without any protective shield of soil to hide the evidence of the past, the history of the landscape and the forces that made it are on show; and every lizard, raven or acacia merely emphasizes the difficulties life has had in adapting to these harsh conditions.

I gathered material for this book in the course of several journeys to the Sahara. One of my earliest memories is of a calm night in the Great Eastern Erg, the sea of sand that covers thousands of square miles in the north-east. Some friends and I had started from the busy market town of El Oued, some 400 miles inland from Algiers, on a journey to the Tassili n Ajjer mountains several hundred miles to the south. The people of El Oued are famous weavers and the shops, capped with barrel vaults or small domes, each had a dozen or more black and brown striped woollen robes hanging outside, together with an occasional camel-hair burnous, the voluminous cloak worn by the desert nomads. The shopkeepers sat in the square, drinking tiny glasses of tea and playing draughts. In one corner a crowd had gathered to watch a fortune-teller as he laid out rows of cards showing Adam and Eve, soldiers on horseback and strange cabalistic signs. I bought a burnous and we drove out of the town in my Land Rover, past gardens dug into the low sand waves lapping at the outskirts.

It was like casting off from a small port, leaving the land behind; indeed, a desert crossing is often like a voyage across open seas. We knew that until we hit the outlying rocks of the Tassili there would be little but sand. As the last remnants of Mediterranean North Africa fell away—a grey shrike on a rock, bushes struggling with the blowing sand—dunes appeared on the horizon, first as a scattering of sandy hills rising from the plain, each isolated from the rest except for an occasional linking ridge of sand, then closer together until one dune was piled on top of another in huge massifs. As the sun went down, the horizon turned violet and then black.

By the time we had made a small camp in the lee of a curved wall of sand, the moon had risen; its light softened the crests of the dunes, throwing out shadows behind ripples of sand and darkening the cols and the high valleys. A tawny owl hooted nearby, disturbed by our presence, and a second owl called to remind the first that it would allow no trespassing across the frontier of its hunting territory. The air was sharp and cold and life was starting in the dunes after the dead heat of the day. I went for a short walk with a torch and surprised a fennec, the small desert fox with large ears, sitting patiently in ambush at a jerboa's hole. He was dazzled for a moment by the light, and his eyes glowed brightly. Then he bounded away up the side of the dune, a pale shape with its own moon shadow. I saw nothing else this first night; the dunes were not going to deliver up all their secrets easily to a day visitor from the civilized world. Wrapping my burnous around me I settled down on a camp bed to admire the stars. In the clear desert air it was easy to see why the ancient Arabs and Persians had been such good astronomers.

In the morning the newspaper of the night's activities was written in the sand around our camp. The fennec tracks purposefully climbed a ridge from the point where I had disturbed him, and then investigated each meagre tuft of vegetation in a hollow on the other side. There were signs of a scuffle, so his search had been rewarded, perhaps by the jerboa whose tracks also circled the tuft. The fennec tracks continued and in a few hundred yards disappeared down a hole in harder sand: he must have been at home, sleeping and sheltering from the heat of the day. Near the hole a lizard-like skink, recognizable by the furrow of his tail with feet on either side, had made heavy weather of a crumbling dune crest. Over the other side his tracks suddenly ended. But he was hiding a few inches down, and I scooped him out. At once he burrowed down again, not digging so much as swimming through the sand with the help of his boat-shaped nose and webbed feet.

In the hollows between the dunes occasional rain must have collected, because there were a few tufts of grass and scattered bushes, each of them an island of life in the barren sand. All the tracks started and ended at these islands, and the bigger bushes had become a busy crossroads for spiders and beetles. Perhaps one of the owls found its meals here. In the days to come I made it my business to spend the first two hours of daylight reading the signs around the camp, to discover the nightly events and dramas of the dune's hidden inhabitants.

This was the desert in its gentlest mood, but in the Sahara such calm is rare. There is more often a strong wind, and the traveller finds himself bent over the wheel of a vehicle or the pommel of a camel saddle, trying to follow a compass bearing or track as the sand begins to blow in tiny rivulets on the ground ahead. Then the desert becomes viciously hostile, and you must make for safety or, if time and resources allow, simply stop and wait out the storm where you are. This lesson was brought home to me one spring in northern Mauritania. With one companion and a relay of nomad guides, I drove north from the river Niger in Mali, heading for the Atlas mountains in Morocco. We were following the ancient route along which caravans had taken sugar, cloth and tea south and brought ostrich feathers, ivory, gold and slaves north in exchange. A few caravans continue today carrying salt and grain, but they are rare, and our only companions were small groups of swallows migrating across the desert to their European nesting grounds.

After two weeks of driving across shifting dunes, making our own route, we reached the gravel plains of northern Mauritania. We were very pleased with ourselves. The worst was over and from now on we were on a well-marked track. We bought camels for the last of our nomad guides to return home and headed north on our own.

Trouble began almost at once. A soldier on sentry duty outside a Mauritanian army fort gave us wrong directions, and by the time it had

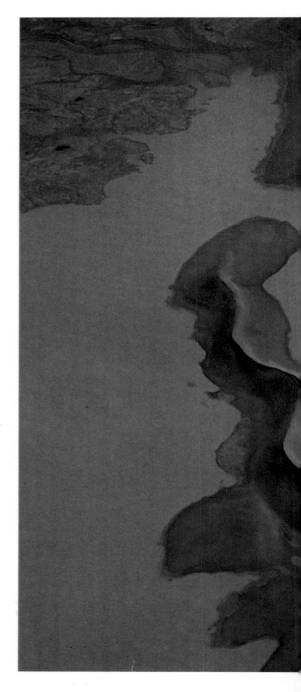

After years of drought, rainwater collects briefly in the hollows between the sand dunes before it is evaporated by the sun.

become clear from the compass readings that we were off course, the vehicle tracks we were following had vanished. Since we were clearly west of the main track, we turned east, thinking that eventually we would hit it. The weather had started to deteriorate. A strong wind was getting up and the air was full of blowing sand and dust, which reduced visibility to a few hundred yards but intensified the sun's heavy glare. Anticipating trouble, we began to keep a dead reckoning chart, noting every change of direction on the compass, together with the number of miles on each bearing. This way we would be able to work out where we were without navigational fixes on the sun.

By now the sand was snaking in little rivulets along the gravel, and even the spiny-tailed uromastix lizards, looking like small crocodiles, which were the only other inhabitants of our hot, ghostly world, had taken refuge in their holes. In the full blast of the storm we had a puncture. By the time we had changed the wheel, there was sand everywhere, inside the Land Rover, inside our clothes. One hour more of driving and we had to recognize that we were lost. Our situation, although not desperate, was dangerous. We knew from the dead reckoning chart that we were about 75 miles north-west of our starting point, but even on a clear day there would be little chance of finding landmarks on this featureless plain. As it was we were enclosed in a hot cocoon of blowing sand and could see almost nothing. Confident at the outset of an easy day's run to the next well, we had taken only two day's water, which had seemed at the time an adequate precaution. In the exertion of mending the tyre and the oppressive heat, we were now drinking much more than usual and quickly running down our precious supply. I hastily transferred the remaining water from the two goatskin guerbas hanging on the side of the Land Rover, which kept their contents cool by evaporation, to a tepid but less wasteful jerrycan. Recognizing the possible consequences of our predicament, my companion and I were tense and exaggeratedly polite to each other as we strained our eyes in the haze for any useful sign—recent vehicle tracks, camels or some topographical feature we could locate on the map.

We decided the safest course was to return to our point of departure. Our own tracks had been quickly obliterated by the wind and blowing sand, so the dead reckoning calculations were our only link with the inhabited world. Adding up all the twists and turns of the morning's journey, I worked out the bearing which should take us back to the fort. For three hours we drove with the compass steady at 155°, using all our strength of mind to resist the temptation to veer off and follow the occasional tyre marks that crossed our path. As evening came, the wind dropped slightly. The dust haze lifted to reveal ahead of us the mud walls of the fort we were searching for.

This comparatively trivial incident was an important lesson not to approach the desert carelessly. There is too much empty space for even quite small navigational errors or casual mistakes. It is difficult for anyone used to the scale of wild places in Europe or America to grasp the sheer size of the Sahara. It is by far the world's largest desert, more than three million square miles, equal in size to the United States and twice as big as Europe west of Russia. Together with the adjacent Libyan Desert, which is merely its continuation to the east, it covers almost the entire northern third of the African continent, from the Atlas mountains in the north to the beginning of the dry savannah fringe of tropical Africa in the south. In the west it reaches to the shores of the Atlantic and in the east, with the sole interruption of the Nile valley, to the coast of the Red Sea. This huge desert occupies about one-sixteenth of the total land area of the earth.

On the map the Sahara has an unreal semblance of occupation. The long straight lines of international frontiers, many of them imposed in the 1950s and 1960s when the French withdrew from their African colonies, parcel it out between Morocco, Algeria, Tunisia, Libya and Egypt in the north and Mauritania, Mali, Niger, Chad and the Sudan in the south. Five main tracks are shown crossing the desert from north to south, with minor tracks branching off. Occasional oases or caravan towns are marked, as well as the half dozen mining centres that have sprung up with the discovery of oil, iron, copper and uranium in recent years. But on the ground the frontiers correspond to no recognizable features of the landscape. The tracks are often little more than the tyre marks of the last vehicle to cross and an occasional stone cairn half buried by sand. The mining towns are tiny, self-sufficient dots in the wilderness, connected by their own airstrips to Europe rather than to the surrounding desert. A few miles off the track or away from the towns, the Sahara is unaffected by the 20th Century.

At the centre of the desert, in southern Algeria, is the Ahaggar mountain chain with peaks of around 9,000 feet. It is surrounded by lesser ranges: in the south, the Adrar n Iforas and Aïr stretch out towards the river Niger and tropical Africa; to the north-east lie the table mountains of the Tassili n Ajjer, dividing the Sahara proper from the Libyan Desert and Egypt, while the Tibesti mountains in northern Chad prolong the mountainous core towards the Sudan and central Africa. Both the ancient granites and volcanic rocks of the Ahaggar and the more recent sandstones of the Tassili are blackened in the desert sun. These sombre and forbidding massifs are the backbone of the Sahara.

Surrounding the Ahaggar and Tassili are the huge gravel plains, called *reg* by the nomads, that cover more than half the Sahara. Composed of fine pebbles or gravel, varying in colour from black to dark red or white, they have very few water-holes and are the most deserted of the desert landscapes. West of the Ahaggar, the Tanezrouft *reg* covers 200,000 square miles and the Libyan *reg* is even larger—340,000 square miles which is an area greater than France and Italy combined. These plains, together with the Ténéré *reg* to the south, dominate the desert and divide it into great sterile and nearly lifeless zones.

Beyond the *reg* are the great concentrations of sand dunes that make an outer ring towards the Sahara's edge. Although the dunes account for only a quarter of the desert surface, they form huge seas of sand, for which the Arabic word is *erg*. In the north lie the Great Eastern and Western Ergs bordering Mediterranean North Africa; in the west, the Erg Chech; and between the Tanezrouft and the Atlantic, the Majabat al-Koubra or Saharan Empty Quarter. South and east of the Tassili n Ajjer mountains are the *ergs* of Bilma and North Chad and the *idehan* of Ubari and Murzuq (*idehan* is the Berber equivalent of *erg*).

The Sahara is a desert for the simple reason that it rains very little there. It lies on the desert belt that encircles the globe between about 15 and 35 degrees north of the equator where wind patterns and the huge distance from the oceans leave the air almost without moisture. Three or four inches of rain a year is generous in the desert. The central regions receive far less, and much of the Sahara does not have a decent shower for more than a year at a time. Some places are extraordinarily dry: Kharga in the Egyptian desert once went 17 years without effective rain. When the rain finally does come, it often falls in violent storms that leave nomad shepherds crouched in sodden burnouses and sometimes spell disaster for oasis towns built of mud brick. In 1922, almost all the mud houses of Tamanrasset, a town in the Ahaggar, collapsed after two and a half days of torrential rain. The population took refuge in the French fort, but a wall collapsed there too, killing eight people.

The harshness of the climate is increased by extremes of hot and cold. The Sahara is not always hot. Frosts are common in the mountains and northern *ergs* in winter, and I have often had to thaw out a frozen water

These inch-long arrowheads collected by the author bear witness to the more temperate Sahara of the past. Several thousand years old, they were chipped out of flint, quartz and a variety of semi-precious stones by neolithic hunters and herdsmen who used them to kill elephants, hippopotamuses, antelopes and ostriches.

skin in order to make breakfast coffee. Sometimes snow falls in the Ahaggar. But for some of the year the Sahara is very hot indeed. Temperatures in the shade, if you can find any, soar to more than 122°F. The exposed surface of the sand and rock gets much hotter still and sand temperatures of over 175°F. have been recorded. The dryness, the heat and the constant Saharan wind combine to evaporate much of the rain that does fall. Potential evaporation over much of the desert reaches 10 or 15 feet a year—this is what would be evaporated in normal conditions by the heat, were such an amount of water to exist. But it does not, of course. There is probably nowhere else outside the polar regions so hostile to most forms of life.

Plants, animals and people have to come to terms with this harsh climate if they are to survive in the Sahara, and few are able to do so. You can travel for a month on a camel without seeing a tree or more than a few tufts of grass. But after rain, desert flowers and grasses suddenly appear, growing and reproducing with urgency before the moisture disappears. Small carpets of flowers spring up in the hollows between dunes or in the gravel plains, and the dunes themselves may take on a greenish hue from a thin covering of ephemeral grass. In the mountains, cracks in the rocks or natural pools in the canyons fill with water, and thorn trees put on green leaves. Animals too are normally inconspicuous. Many are buff or sand-coloured and merge imperceptibly into the dune landscape. Others come out only at night and spend the day in burrows or in loose sand a few inches beneath the surface.

This knowledge that a secret life is going on creates a feeling of mystery about the Sahara, which is deepened by the fact that everywhere in this desert are signs of intense human activity far in the past. There are large conical tombs made of piled rocks, and drawings and paintings on rock surfaces, showing herds of piebald cattle and ritual scenes whose participants wear strange head-dresses and body decoration. In some areas stone-age axes, arrow-heads and fish harpoons lie so thick on the ground that you can walk about and pick up half a dozen in a few minutes. There are fossilized fish bones in the middle of arid wastes where it now rains once in ten years. At times the desert looks like an inhabited landscape suddenly abandoned one afternoon thousands of years ago.

There is little historical information about these early inhabitants of the desert. The Greek historian Herodotus wrote about troglodytes in the Sahara hunted by warriors in horse-drawn chariots, and Egyptian geographers were interested in what lay to the west. But this was never more than speculation. Strange stories circulated about the beasts that lived in the desert: snakes that leapt from trees like javelins, lizards with heads at both ends of their bodies and, the most fabulous of all, the basilisk whose stare turned men to stone. Arab travellers from the 10th Century onwards obtained more reliable information as they crossed the desert with trading caravans carrying slaves, eunuchs and civet musk, but Europe remained ignorant. Medieval mapmakers were forced to write "Here are lions" to fill up the empty space (they were not being fanciful—there were lions in the arid steppe on the northern and southern edges of the desert), and until the 19th Century the Sahara was shown as a uniformly sandy waste stretching from the Mediterranean to what was called Negroland.

Rumour was responsible for the beginning of European interest in the Sahara. Powerful empires like Ghana and Mali had existed on the southern edge of the desert in the Middle Ages, rich in gold and in salt from Saharan mines. When the Emperor of Mali, Mansa Musa, went on a pilgrimage to Mecca in 1324, he was preceded by 500 slaves each carrying a golden staff and he had with him 100 camels laden with gold, which he distributed lavishly. Stories of this magnificence were wildly exaggerated in the retelling. The houses in Timbuktu were said to be roofed with gold, and the city was thought not only to be a great centre of Arabic learning but also to contain lost Greek and Roman classical manuscripts. Societies were formed in Britain to trade with such wealthy peoples, and a generation of European explorers attempted to cross the Sahara to make contact. Many did not survive. Those who did, like Réné Caillé and Heinrich Barth who reached Timbuktu in 1828 and 1853 respectively, returned with disappointing descriptions of houses roofed not in gold but in mud. They also provided the first reliable reports of the desert and its inhabitants, especially the Tuareg nomads who resisted European penetration and killed some of the explorers.

Tuareg still occupy a large part of the central Sahara, and their hidden presence is often as mysterious as that of the plants and animals. Signs of them—camel tracks, heavily grazed tufts of grass and thorn bushes, abandoned tent poles—are common, but it may be days before you find a camp. Then, sleeping out near a dry wadi, you may hear the sounds of animals, the deep groaning of camels and the bleating of goats in the night. Sometimes you can detect the dull thump of *tinde* drumming, as the women of the tribe beat the rhythm with their hands on wet leather stretched and bound tightly across the top of a grain mortar.

I heard these sounds one evening in the Aïr mountains. As I was settling down to supper, four small Tuareg children filed shyly out of the darkness and came to sit huddled together just beyond the range of my camp fire. The eldest boy fetched a branch for the fire, and I gave them part of the meal, which they ate in a puzzled manner. They watched every movement of pitching camp attentively, craning their necks in unison to follow my movements. Later, before I went to sleep, they filed silently away again into the darkness. But at first light they were back again with a wrinkled old woman, and this time one of them was carrying a wooden bowl of goat's milk, which he put down by the embers of the fire for me to drink. They all sat close together some distance away, watching. Later I visited their camp of five low red leather tents. The men were dressed in voluminous blue robes and black or indigo-blue head veils, and some of them carried long straight swords in decorated red leather scabbards.

Tuareg such as these live largely on milk from their herds; they move with their animals from one threadbare pasture to another, following the pattern of rain but usually returning to the same well each dry season. It is a difficult existence and the Tuareg own no more than can easily be carried on a camel or donkey, but their way of life is as well adapted to the harsh desert conditions as that of the animals and plants.

Tuareg camps have always attracted me, and I have lived in them for several months at a time. Life in the desert, and especially in the nomad camps where the protective shield of Western technology is reduced to the barest essentials, was for me a lesson in ecological humility. To rely on the resources of the desert is often not easy and is occasionally very disagreeable indeed. But for the person who takes the plunge, sleeps out under the stars and adjusts his activity to the rhythms of the desert, the rewards are great. The simplicity of this life and its frequent pleasures enable you to understand why Théodore Monod, the greatest living Saharan traveller, wrote of this as "the largest, most beautiful, most perfect desert in the world".

The Rock Fabric

Only a quarter of the Sahara is covered by sand dunes. Most of it is a mosaic of mountains and plains where the ancient crystalline rock base of the desert has been shaped and reshaped over millions of years to form a variety of different geological materials ranging from the hardest continental rock to gravel and—of course—sand.

The oldest rocks visible in the Sahara are crystalline—like granite and schist—which were fused by massive heat and pressure a few thousand million years ago. Most of them lie buried in the basement of the Sahara, thousands of feet beneath the surface, but in the chaotic jumble of the Ahaggar and Tibesti mountains they have been exposed, revealing a hard surface scarred with cracks (right). Some cracks opened as the rock cooled, others when covering rocks were peeled off by erosion. They were worn into crevices by percolating water.

Above the Sahara's hard crystalline base lie a variety of sedimentary rocks such as sandstone and limestone, laid down in successive eras when prehistoric seas, lakes and marshes covered the area. These sediments are made largely from second-hand fragments of granite

and other old rocks, broken down by weathering, re-sorted by water and then re-cemented.

Saharan sandstone creates a landscape quite unlike the mounds and domes of the granite features: in the Tassili n Ajjer mountains, for example, it has been eroded into fretted pinnacles and turrets, and canyons carved deeply by rushing water. In most places its yellowish surface has been blackened by the effects of the sun and polished by wind-blown sand.

Still younger Saharan rocks such as basalts were thrust to the surface two million years ago when volcanic eruptions shook the Ahaggar and Tibesti. Lava was heaped hundreds of feet thick on the hard crystalline basement and flowed in streams down the mountain valleys. When the volcanoes became inactive, most of their cones were eroded away to reveal spectacular fluted pillars of basalt that had solidified inside.

These rocky uplands, a prey to the erosion of centuries, were the source of huge quantities of gravel and sand. Fragments prized off by weathering were ground down and strewn by rivers on desolate plains. The sand was then winnowed out by the wind into shifting seas of dunes.

A sheet of granite in the Ahaggar mountains is scarred by a large crack, formed when the rock cooled and then later gouged out by erosion.

Volcanic plugs stick up through the crystalline rocks of the Ahaggar mountains as evidence of great upheavals far in the past. More than two million years ago, volcanoes erupted, built cones of ash and other debris thrown up by the explosions and filled the valleys with lava flows. When the volcanoes became extinct, lava solidified in their central channels or "chimneys". After the cones were eroded away, the harder contents of the chimneys remained as hills and peaks dominating the landscape.

The tops of basalt columns look almost man-made against the jagged outcrops of granite above.

In the Ahaggar, columns of basaltic lava that stand intact like organ pipes on the skyline have elsewhere collapsed into a mass of rubble.

The blackened surface of eroded sandstone columns gives the Tassili n Ajjer mountains a baked appearance in keeping with the harshness of the climate. The colour, the so-called desert varnish, comes largely from traces of iron and manganese brought to the surface after rain. As the rocks dry in the intense heat of the desert sun, these minerals are drawn up in the evaporating moisture. On contact with the air they oxidize and harden to a dark patina.

Coarsely ground sediments, swept out and deposited by meandering prehistoric rivers, form the rough pavement of a gravel plain or reg.

At the farthest extremity of the reg, the rivers have deposited finer stones, their edges smoothed by the erosive action of the water.

Huge quantities of sand form a fluid
landscape of crests and valleys in a
sand sea or erg of central Algeria. The
winds constantly sculpt the sand,
creating the curving lines of dunes and
in places sweeping it into mountains
that may be up to 1,000 feet high.

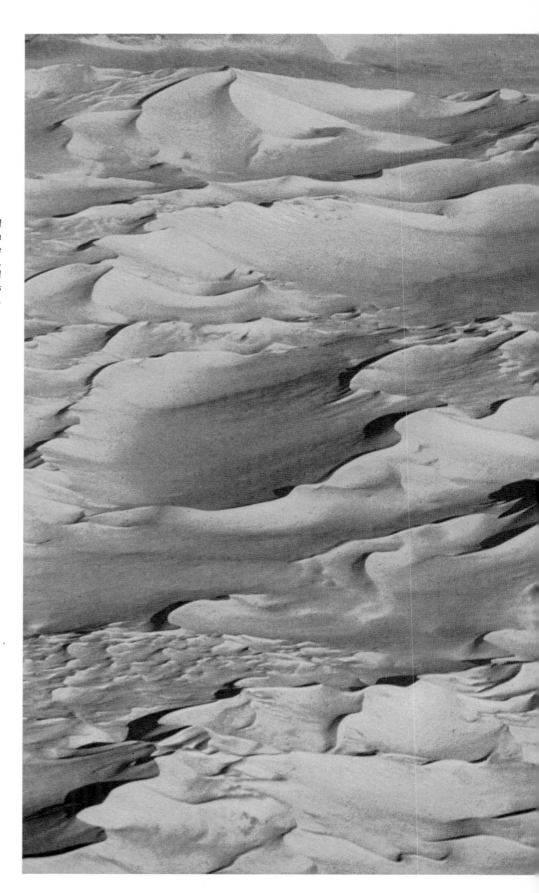

2/ The Mark of Vanished Waters

Sand taken from sandstone which itself was constructed of quartz crystals deriving from older granites. . . . Everything has changed, everything still changes, imperceptibly, irresistibly.

THEODORE MONOD/ *A LA RENCONTRE DE L'AFRIQUE DE L'OUEST*

It is almost impossible to grasp the full meaning of geological time. People remember the events of recent years, and have some knowledge of modern history, but the Pharaohs or the Han dynasty seem unbelievably far in the past. Geological time makes a mockery of all this. While the history of civilizations is measured in thousands of years, the age of rocks and fossils is measured in hundreds of millions of years. The main Saharan plateaux, the sandstones, are up to 500 million years old. And they are young by the standards of the underlying continental shield, which was formed 2,000 million years ago.

In the Sahara you are continually reminded of these facts in a manner that makes them intelligible. Without soil, greenery or signs of human activity, the evidence of hundreds of millions of years of geological change is laid out like an open textbook. In the crystalline mountains of the Ahaggar or Tibesti, you can read the past: conical mountains and sharp peaks betray the position of long-extinct volcanoes, and more level stretches amid the volcanic debris mark the line taken by flowing lava as it filled valleys and smothered much more ancient hills and ridges. In other parts of the desert, the past is even more clearly before your eyes. Dry river beds, deep canyons, sandstone and limestone formations that can only have been created by water, are all reminders that the Sahara was once very different from the desert today. It has been successively a sea, a tropical forest and a savannah watered by

rivers and lakes. The evidence of climatic fluctuations is visible for anyone to see, not only in the landscape itself, but also in fossilized animal
bones, in prehistoric cave paintings and stone tools, and in species
of plants and animals that seem out of place in a desert.

The base of the Sahara is a dense, rigid shield of crystalline rocks,
scrubbed almost flat by erosion and so strong that it resisted most of the
later upheavals that produced mountains in younger geological regions.
Only in the centre of the Sahara did it give way to gentle updoming.
Movements from beneath distorted the ancient shield, creating the
foundations of the Ahaggar, Aïr, Adrar n Iforas and Tibesti ranges. The
fault lines left weaknesses through which volcanoes were able to erupt
thousands of years later.

Since the underlying shield is mostly buried beneath the Sahara, the
ancient crystalline rocks can only be seen in the mountains. One of the
best places to go is the Ahaggar. It is a mysterious and sinister place and
it is easy to see why it was known to Arab travellers as "the country of
fear". I approached it from the east where gravel plains give way slowly
to low rock domes and cones, as uniformly black as the gravel plain
from which they rise. It was December and the sky was overcast with
grey clouds. An occasional silver sunbeam filtered through them,
lighting up the hills with subtle shades of silver, grey and black like a
Dutch master's study of light reflected in pewter and silver dishes. To
the north, the clouds were more menacing, although they were shot
through with a small rainbow.

As I drove westwards, the rudimentary track, marked every mile or
two by a small stone cairn, began to rise. The black volcanic rocks gave
way to the mixed colours of granites: greys, and surprising pastel pinks
and purples, which changed with the light. A rock that would hardly
have been noticeable in the dusty heat of midday came alive in the softer
tones of evening. Granite boulders were piled on top of one another and
weathered into shapes so smooth and delicate that it seemed a breath of
wind could topple them to the ground. They had, of course, been there
too long to be shaken. Some had eroded like artichokes, their thin
surface layers peeling away to reveal a new surface as smooth as the old.
It was easy to imagine these huge boulders to be the architecture of a
race of giants. "Who else," my Tuareg guide said to me, "could pile one
rock on top of another in such a manner?"

The track climbed among these rocks, leaving them behind, and the
country opened out into a huge lava field. Lumps of black volcanic
pumice were evenly spread, disturbed only by an occasional meandering

The stark, volcanic plug of Ilamen (right) stands out in the early morning haze. Behind it are a range of basalt peaks, which are also the remains of the violent eruptions that gave the Atakor mountains their jagged skyline.

ribbon of white sand where generations of camels, following the same path, had kicked the stones aside. The lava field was not level, and in one of the hollows a broad wadi bed marked the course of an ancient river. The green grasses and tamarisk trees and the clear white sand were a welcome respite from the lifeless black rocks all around, and we camped for the night, knowing that there would be an ample supply of branches for firewood against the cold.

The following day I continued towards the Atakor mountains at the heart of the Ahaggar range. It was at once apparent that the Atakor were created by volcanic activity. The rough track rose rapidly into a weird landscape of rock spurs, pinnacles and saw-tooth crests, contrasting with the sugar-loaf domes of the granite. The surface of the whole massif had been so bent, folded and turned back on itself that the layers of rock and the parallel joints where it had broken under tension ran as often vertically as horizontally, and in places were bent into graceful curves. All the rock was black or dark grey, its crumbled surface naked and unprotected by soil or vegetation.

At the centre of this desolate mass, an extraordinary range of peaks dominated the landscape: Tahat, at over 9,000 feet the tallest mountain of the Ahaggar; the saddle-like col of Assekrem; Ilamen, a vertical finger of rock formed from an old volcanic core, and many others. I climbed Assekrem to get a better view. As far as the eye could see, there was nothing but blackness: black hills, black cliffs, black rock needles, black plateaux and lava fields. The only bird I saw that morning was a black raven, as though the blackness of the landscape had impressed itself on the living inhabitants. The desolate effect of this monotony of colour was emphasised by the disorder of the mountains and rocks. Different shapes jostled together, and half the landscape seemed to have collapsed into huge piles of rubble. If the granite boulders we had seen earlier were the architecture of the giants, the Atakor was a ruined city of titans, a city destroyed by earthquakes.

Even the Tuareg nomads who live in the Atakor are impressed by the scenery and they have invested these peaks with mythical personalities, involving them in complicated and nomad-like love stories. Mount Ilamen is said to have been wounded in a jealous brawl with the husband of another mountain. Learning from his mistake, he fell in love with Mount Tahat who was unattached and moved closer to her, leaving behind in his haste a circular crater as evidence of his original position. An unsuccessful rival for Tahat's affections slunk off leaving no trace, and is to this day morosely planted in the desolate gravel plain of the Tanezrouft.

At the top of Assekrem there is a small chapel made of black rocks taken from the surrounding mountains. It was built in 1911 by a French monk and mystic, Charles de Foucauld, who came here at the beginning of the French occupation of the central Sahara in order to study the Tuareg way of life. De Foucauld was killed in 1916 by the nomads when they revolted against the French. The voluminous dictionary of the Tuareg language he compiled is still a standard reference work, used by all subsequent researchers. Assekrem is a site you would expect such a man to have chosen: a wild and remote place in the tradition of Benedictine and Taoist retreats, without worldly distractions but with the wonders of the natural landscape perpetually before your eyes.

Away from the crystalline mountains, the ancient shield rocks are buried under the more common desert landscapes formed by water: sand, gravel and flat-topped sedimentary mountains. Water is the essential tool by which landscapes are made, and paradoxically most Saharan landforms owe their shapes to its power. Without it a landscape is frozen into immobility, dead to all but the smallest changes. Water soaks into rock or penetrates by small cracks. It dissolves some substances and starts chemical reactions in others. During cold winter nights it freezes and expands, splintering the rocks like burst pipes. Water carries the fragments away, sieves the gravel and sand and deposits them in basins where they form new sedimentary rocks. Throughout the Sahara's history, an endless, millennial game was played, as the same basic constituents, consisting of particles eroded from the ancient continental shield, were ground down, carried away by rivers, deposited in seas or lakes elsewhere, and turned to rock—only to be eroded to sand and gravel once more. The same sand may have changed its form several times during those long epochs, from rock to dune and back to rock.

During the Carboniferous period some 250 million years ago, a vast sea flooded most of the desert. Debris eroded from the ancient shield was deposited on the sea floor, forming some of the Sahara's main sandstone ranges, including the Tassili n Ajjer. The sea was replaced when, in a long continental phase, marshes, lakes and dry land turned the Sahara into an archaic paradise. Dinosaurs inhabited its tropical forests, and the fossils of both animals and trees can be found now in the Ténéré and the Tidikelt. By the Cretaceous, 130 million years ago, they had gone, and the sea again covered large parts of the north and south, although not the whole Sahara. These seas withdrew in turn, to be replaced again by lakes and marshes. Sandstone and limestone were deposited in this period, in particular the limestone plateaux of the northern desert.

Since the Cretaceous, there has been no sea in the Sahara, but the land has not always been dry. Rainfall, and thus the geological processes that are influenced by rain, was affected by climatic fluctuations similar to those that caused the ice ages in Europe. The result was a succession of less dramatic wet and dry periods in which huge lakes and rivers with rich plant and animal life alternated with lifeless desert and mountains. But the Sahara already had its desert vocation, and the wetter phases were merely interludes in a long, dry evolution. Since the time of the dinosaurs there has been no lush tropical paradise there. Indeed, during one of the dry periods, the desert was much larger than it is now: a belt of sand dunes, now anchored by vegetation, lies well to the south of the present desert edge, in some places stretching 300 miles into tropical Africa. The desert has also been much smaller: ten or 20 thousand years ago two large lakes gave the southern Sahara a very different aspect. Megachad, as large as the Caspian, extended 400 miles north of the present banks of Lake Chad. In the west, the Niger flowed into a closed basin north of Timbuktu to form Lake Arawan; only much later did the water level in this lake rise high enough to break through the sill to the south-east and follow the bed of what is now the lower Niger, giving the river its characteristic twisted course.

The generally centrifugal character of the Sahara, with the mountains at the centre and the gravel plains and sand seas spread out beyond, is the product of this long evolution since the sea retreated for the last time. None of the ancient Saharan rivers had outlets to the oceans. They flowed down from the central mountain spine into closed basins, depositing the debris of erosion to form gravel plains or reg. In the dry periods the wind winnowed out the sand to form the sand seas or ergs, farther out towards the desert's edge.

The major fashioning of the landscape ceased long ago as the Sahara dried up, but minor modifications of the rock by water, wind and sun continue. The easiest way to understand how the underlying structure of the desert has been modelled and decorated on the surface into the shapes we see today, is to climb into one of the sandstone plateaux. In November 1973, I spent a few days in the Fadnoun plateau, which forms the northern spur of the Tassili n Ajjer range. The first impression was of bleak desolation, a chaos of black rock and rubble, cut at intervals by deep, lifeless ravines. During the day the naked rock radiated heat in the white sunlight, but in the evening the sun went early behind the hills and shadows lengthened behind the line of crests, each one blacker than the one behind. This changing landscape of light and shade gave a certain liveliness to an otherwise dead mountain range.

The top of the plateau was flat but in places it had been eroded into rows of sandstone blocks like the crest of a stone monster. Elsewhere sheer canyons cut into bedrock a few tens of yards across but a thousand feet deep. The sides of one were sheer for most of its length, but at one end were further eroded into a haphazard array of fluted pillars. Some of the rock was solid, a careful juxtaposition of substantial blocks, but there was no overriding pattern; elsewhere thousands of wafer-thin layers of sandstone were cut and eroded into tiny ravines and cirques.

The original rock was coloured a warm terracotta, but wherever it was exposed to the sun it had burned to a dark varnish, so the whole plateau was a mottled dark grey. The lack of other colours and the barrenness of the rock was extraordinary, and after a few days I craved bright colours and some sign of life. Although the sandstone appeared as hard as normal rock, underneath it was often so soft that a lump crumbled when thrown to the ground. Such a chaotic, disintegrating, black landscape would have been desolate on a small scale; so large, it was magnificent.

The apparent chaos of the plateau began to sort itself out in my mind as I realized how much it was the product of the sun, wind and water—especially the last of these. The lack of any covering of soil or plants meant not only that the elements worked directly on the rock, but also that the results of their action were everywhere visible. A wadi bed several miles long was the key to the sort of processes that had shaped the whole plateau.

Although it was now dry and dusty, the wadi had clearly been created by water, and at some stage a powerful stream had cut its way through the rocks, gouging a channel around the bigger boulders and pushing the smaller ones aside or breaking them down into fragments. Because the rock surface for miles around the wadi was flat and bare, any rain that fell would collect here rapidly from a huge catchment area, digging the wadi deeper and wider with a powerful bore. For a few hours this dusty little channel would be filled with a wild torrent carrying everything movable with it. It was easy to imagine how great the force of the wadi water would have been with the more abundant rain of the past. Thousands of years of this relentless activity had cleaned and scrubbed the plateau down to its rocky skeleton.

Wind and sun add the finishing touches to the work of the water. Persistent and often sand-laden, the wind erodes characteristic hollows and grooves, and wears down projecting outcrops until only an aerodynamic shark's fin is left. I saw only small fins in the Fadnoun, but in northern Chad these *yardangs*, as they are called by geologists, may be 600 feet high and half a mile long; they are oriented in the same northeast/south-west direction as the small sand dunes of the area, a tribute to the power and constancy of the wind. The wind also gouges out long parallel grooves. These are usually small, but in the Tibesti they may be up to half a mile across, curving around the flanks of mountains for long distances along the line of the prevailing wind.

Wind may also polish the rocks to produce a shiny patina, but the sombre colours of most Saharan rocks have a chemical origin. The dark surface, known as desert varnish, is a thin layer, varying in colour from a shiny black of almost lacquer-like intensity to a dull maroon. When rain wets the rock, capillary action brings solutions of iron and manganese to the surface where they are oxidized by the sun. Some minerals may also come from weathered rubble surrounding the varnished surface. Sandstone varnishes best but limestone has an unstable sur-

A river once flowed through this wadi in the Tassili mountains, carving out the sandstone and carrying away debris to the plains below.

face and the varnish is eroded away almost as quickly as it forms. On rocks where it persists, varnish acts as an armour against further erosion, and in some places may have lasted as much as 50,000 years. But you can also see varnish beginning to form on rocks exposed to the sun and weather only ten or 15 years ago.

Mountain ranges built up and worn down; the same materials fusing, breaking up and fusing again in different places and in different combinations; the endless dialectic of sedimentation and erosion—all this is on show wherever one travels in the desert.

In the north, sedimentary limestone forms great tables of rock, or *hamadas*, from which most of the loose debris has been removed by the wind and water. In places a firmly rooted sand and clay soil allows a few stunted bushes to grow, and the plateau may be strewn with boulders too large to be moved by these forces. The water running off some of the cliffs cuts deep erosion channels in the sand or rock beneath. Below some *hamadas*, the drainage water is rich in chemicals and has formed small salt pans. Seen from above, they look like mud-flats with the tide out; dry channels meander through red, green and white crusts in which crystalline shapes form and dissolve.

In many sandstone ranges, the edge of the plateau has been eaten away by the forces of water and wind and a line of rock columns may be left behind. These *garas*, as they are called, are often in an advanced state of decay themselves, with piles of debris around their bases. A row of *garas* in a completely flat plain—the isolated rearguard of a retreating mountain—is a characteristic Saharan sight.

In the western desert, low sandstone cliffs, formed when the sedimentary rock covering broke and tilted, break a plain otherwise monotonously flat for hundreds of thousands of square miles. The longest of these cliffs, or *dhars* as they are called in Mauritania, run for several hundred miles in an unbroken wall. They are important features for travellers. If your route lies along them they are useful navigation aids, but they are often difficult to climb or cross although rarely more than a few hundred feet high. And when you have painfully made your way to the top there is no new mountain scenery, but merely more of the sand or gravel you had left behind at the bottom.

People first entered the picture very recently on the geological time scale. The earliest signs of human occupation are palaeolithic tools, dating probably from several hundred thousand years ago. A site in the Tihodaine Erg, north of the Ahaggar, shows what life must have been like

These petrified tree trunks, found at In Gall in the southern Sahara, date from the time of luxuriant tropical forests 100 million years ago. After the trees fell and sank into soft ground, their branches decayed. But the thick trunks absorbed silica with underground water, solidified and were entombed as the surrounding sediments turned to rock. After many millennia they were exhumed by the erosive forces of wind and water.

in the Sahara then, during one of the wet periods. There were hunters' camps beside a fresh-water marsh, and hand axes can still be found on the sand alongside bones of white rhinoceros, elephant, zebra and hippo. As the wet period ended, these early inhabitants of the desert were probably forced to cluster around the shrinking lakes and marshes, destined to die along with the animals they preyed upon. But each dry phase ended eventually, the wadis and lakes filled again, and fish and wild animals returned. Hunters and fishermen followed them, often reoccupying the sites that had been inhabited a hundred thousand years before. Profiting by the mild climate, a typically Mediterranean vegetation spread southwards from North Africa over the whole of the central Sahara. By about 4000 B.C., parts of the desert as far south as the Tibesti and Aïr mountains were rather improbably covered with Mediterranean scrub. Trees such as maple, ash, walnut and lime were common in the mountains.

Striking evidence of this recent Saharan past· survives in rock paintings and engravings dating from the first half of the sixth millennium B.C. which have been discovered all over the Saharan mountains. I was unprepared for the sophistication of these engravings the first time I saw them. I was setting up camp for the night in the Adrar n Iforas mountains on the Algerian-Mali border, when a Tuareg friend with me casually mentioned that there were "old drawings" on the rocks some distance behind us. We at once went to look for them in the evening sunlight.

A ridge of black rock stood at the edge of a wadi. The rock was broken into huge blocks, which were covered in engravings cut into the surface so that the pale colours of the stone beneath contrasted with the shiny black covering of desert varnish. A giraffe several feet tall occupied the whole of one face, while on the others there was a jumble of smaller drawings. Oryx and ostriches raced around one corner, almost colliding with a mounted horseman carrying a shield. Nearby were the enigmatic figures of several horse-drawn war-chariots, shown from above with the wheels spread out on either side.

The artists of the earliest period of Saharan art were presumably the early neolithic men who hunted giraffe and elephant in the dry savannah that then covered much of the desert, or pursued hippo and fish in the lakes and rivers. These hunting pictures were replaced by numerous pictures of cattle, as nomadic cattle herdsmen moved into the desert from the east, perhaps from the Upper Nile. For a time there must have been a great pastoral civilization in the Sahara, making use of the abundant Mediterranean vegetation. But around 2700 B.C. the climate changed again; rainfall diminished, the rivers and marshes dried up. In the paintings, cattle and their herdsmen are gradually supplanted by warriors mounted on horses or travelling in horse-drawn chariots. It seems likely that military or commercial routes were opened across the Sahara as early as 1000 B.C.

The desert landscape was already changing by the time the warrior invaders arrived. Under the influence of a drier climate, Mediterranean vegetation was replaced by thorn trees from the tropical African steppes in the south, and the Mediterranean plants survived only in the mountains. As rainfall diminished even the hardy thorn vegetation gave way. Horses, driven out of the desert by worsening conditions like the cattle before them, disappear from the paintings. Camels were reintroduced into the Sahara (they were there much earlier, but had become extinct) at the time of the Roman occupation of North Africa in the 2nd Century A.D. By the 4th Century, many nomads in the desert had camels, and they become common in the paintings. Camels enabled life to continue in the face of increasing hardship but, by eating all the edible plants that served to anchor down the sand, they probably hastened the progressive transformation of the Sahara into desert.

Further evidence of recent climatic change comes from relict plants and trees left behind when the present dry period began over 3,000 years

Fingers of sand reach into Wanyanga Serir, a salt lake 120 miles southeast of the Tibesti mountains. Thousands of years ago the lake was much larger and was fed by a river whose delta has long since turned to dry sand. When the river ceased to flow, the lake began to evaporate. Its sandstone islands (foreground) became encrusted with salt, and it was left unprotected from the wind-blown sand that may one day completely smother it.

ago. High up in the Tassili and Ahaggar mountains, at the edge of rock pools, are Mediterranean oleanders, separated from the Mediterranean by more than 1,000 miles of inhospitable desert.

There are olive trees too. Laperrine's olive, named after the most famous French Saharan soldier, is found above 5,000 feet in most of the mountain ranges as far south as Jebel Marra in the Sudan. Among the black rocks, their twisted trunks stretch 30 or 40 feet up to catch the sunlight, the bark split and folded as though the trees had been flayed. But some olives on Greboun in the Aïr mountains measure more than nine feet round the trunk. In order to have grown to this size, they may be 3,000 or 4,000 years old. These Saharan olives do not reproduce any more, but vegetate passively.

The most striking of the relict trees are the Duprez cypresses of the Tassili, also named after a French army officer. There are no more than 60 or 70 left, and they too are very old, surviving with the help of huge roots that dig into the rock to traces of moisture deep beneath. Often they are twisted into contorted shapes as though the effort put into simple survival has made normal growth impossible. Like the olives, the Tassili cypresses no longer reproduce themselves; however the seeds produce fine trees if taken back and planted in the Mediterranean.

Other evidence of better times in the Sahara is provided by some animals of the *gueltas* or permanent rock pools scattered through the main mountain ranges. The conditions in the pools do not change much from century to century and some unlikely animals are still in residence, unaffected by the surrounding desert. Fish, frogs, toads, shrimps, molluscs and small crustaceans can all be found; insects and dragonflies, which supply food for migrating birds, are common.

I sat in the rocks above a *guelta* in the Fadnoun for half a day once, watching the comings and goings. The pool was on one side of a narrow wadi, cut canyon-like into the sandstone. Around it sheer cliffs rose several hundred feet, shading the green water from the sun and preventing it from being evaporated away. Around the pool, crocus-like plants were growing and there were footprints of a hyrax that had slipped on the wet mud while drinking and had climbed back up the slope with difficulty. The hyrax—the coney of the Bible—is a rabbit-sized, virtually tail-less animal, but it is related to the elephant. Hyraxes live in colonies in rocks in many of the Saharan mountains, but are very shy and difficult to see. I was not lucky that day, and the tracks around the *guelta* were already quite old.

Above the water a pair of pale crag martins circled, their flight a mixture of effortless gliding and powerful swerving dashes among the rocks. Suddenly the air was full of melodious sound and 20 swallows dived in a tight flock down from the sky into the funnel of rock above the *guelta*. Each took a sip of water, gliding down to touch the surface, then they all swirled above the water, hunting insects. For a moment the air was full of swallows and the crag martins were eclipsed. Then, suddenly silent, the swallows left to continue their migration south.

The following day I visited the nearby *gueltas* of Iherir in a sandstone canyon. Here a dozen Tuareg families were living in stone huts among palm trees in cultivated groves. The walls of the canyon were so precipitous that when a dog appeared from one of the huts to scare me off, its single plaintive bark echoed back for several seconds afterwards as if there were a pack of ferocious hounds in the rocks. Even the dog, an unassuming oasis mongrel, seemed startled by this dramatic effect; visitors to be barked at were obviously rare here.

The *gueltas* beyond the village are famous, for they once sheltered the most unlikely animal to have survived from wetter times. In 1876, the German explorer, Erwin von Bary, visited the *gueltas* and was astonished to find crocodile tracks in the wet mud banks. He died at Ghat in Libya the following year before he could investigate further, but his diary was published. In a note, the editor pointed out that since von Bary was a trained naturalist, the existence of crocodiles in the central Sahara could not be doubted. They did indeed exist: one of them was shot by a French army captain in 1908 and its skeleton is now displayed in a museum in Algiers. It is only six feet long, as though the desert could not support anything larger. Probably the Iherir crocodiles were at the end of their time for by the 1930s there were none left. There are still some in remote *gueltas* in the Tibesti and Mauritania, but how long these relics of the past can survive is uncertain.

The Once-Green Sahara

The Sahara has not always been a desert to the same extent as today. Over the last two million years it has fluctuated several times between even greater aridity and comparative greenness. Where there are now dry gullies, rivers once flowed; in what are now empty plains, there were lakes, some very large, surrounded by grasslands and trees.

Wild animals flourished on the vegetation of the green Sahara, and as long ago as the sixth millenium B.C. there were human populations living better than the austere camel nomads of today. They left vivid evidence of the climatic and ecological changes of the Sahara in thousands of rock paintings and engravings, which can still be seen in the mountain massifs they inhabited, above all in the Tassili n Ajjer plateau, where these photographs were taken.

The pictures are in a mixture of styles, from crude engravings to exquisitely painted scenes of men hunting, and women and children playing. The person who has done most to study and date Tassili art is a Frenchman, Henri Lhote, who led his first expedition to the plateau in 1956. Basing his conclusions on the animals shown in the pictures and on rock art known elsewhere in the desert, Lhote speculated that there had been three main periods of Saharan life before present desert conditions arrived.

The earliest period, which appears to have started before 5000 B.C., is characterized by pictures mainly of wild animals, evidence that the area was inhabited by hunters. Then, from about 4000 B.C. to 2000 B.C. or later, the hunters were replaced by people who tended large herds of domestic cattle and painted in a fine naturalistic style.

In about 1200 B.C., when the Sahara was opened up by trade or military expeditions from the north, the horse was introduced and the Sahara became drier. Camels appeared at the start of the Christian era, eventually replacing both cattle and horses—an indication that desert conditions were becoming dominant. The life-supporting vegetation thinned out—probably as a result of long-term climatic change intensified by overgrazing—and the Saharan peoples had to migrate. Today the mountains are empty, save for the inhabitants of the oases and the nomads who sometimes set up camp in the caves that were home to their predecessors long ago.

Two hunters from prehistory dominate the smooth, eroded wall of a shallow cave in the Tassili plateau. Arrowheads and bones, relics of the chase thousands of years ago, may still be found on the sandy floors of shelters such as this.

A Prehistoric Safari

In the engravings and paintings of the earliest period of Tassili art, the wildlife of the green Sahara is depicted as abundant and amazingly diverse. Six or seven thousand years ago, in early neolithic times, a journey through the Sahara would have been very much like a safari in the game parks of sub-Saharan Africa today. Giraffe, ostrich, elephant, rhinoceros, buffalo, lion, leopard, warthog and many species of antelope and gazelle roamed the savannah and wooded uplands (which, on the evidence of fossilized pollen grains, supported wild olive, alder, lime, holm oak and cypress). Crocodiles and hippopotamuses swam in the many rivers and lagoons.

The earliest pictures of this period, dating back to the first half of the sixth millenium B.C., are engravings, made by scratching and gouging the rock face with stone tools. Later on, simple outline or solid-colour paintings appear.

Judging by this style (often similar to prehistoric tribal art found in other parts of Africa) and the appearance of the human figures that are featured in some paintings of this period, the first Saharans were probably of Negroid stock.

Since no domestic animals appear in their pictures, these early inhabitants were probably hunters. No doubt they were also gatherers and, like hunting people today, ate the fruits of trees, grass seeds and other edible plants from the rich vegetation around them.

A woman of 5000 B.C. bears markings like the decorative scars of some tribesmen today.

This antelope is painted in the solid-colour early Saharan style.

A crudely drawn leopard is seen in apparent pursuit of an ostrich.

Elephants were once common, as this engraving indicates, but their huge food needs put them at a disadvantage when desiccation began.

On some rock faces in the Tassili plateau, different styles have been painted over each other, providing a clue to the sequence of periods in Saharan life. In the picture below, the pair of Negroid hunters and the crude paintings from the earliest period have been partly covered with finely detailed mouflon, reflecting the transition to the style of the succeeding age, with its sophisticated scenes of herding life (right).

The replacement of the Sahara's early hunters by herdsmen is marked by the appearance of domestic animals in the rock art of the Tassili (below). From about 4000 B.C. sheep and goats were depicted in upland caves and cattle were painted almost everywhere, especially in the valleys, which must then have been carpeted with grass. These herds provided the basis for the golden age of Saharan life (overleaf).

The Golden Age

The most sophisticated of Tassili paintings, accurate in detail and remarkably life-like, are those of the cattle-herding period; they reflect the highest civilization produced by the central Sahara. The people who painted them, perhaps emigrants from farther east, lived on the plateau for more than two millennia. On the evidence of the pictures, which mostly depict cows, calves and herdsmen, their economy was soundly based on domestic cattle, from which they obtained milk, leather and meat.

These pastoralists clearly enjoyed an easy life. In many scenes they are playing, dancing or simply sitting in conversation. In others they are out hunting, for there was still plenty of wildlife to provide sport and a change of diet.

Painting was evidently an important part of their culture, perhaps because they had time on their hands and could afford the luxury of unproductive work. In addition, the plentiful supplies of art materials that could be derived from sandstone must have been a natural encouragement. They made paint by grinding the red, yellow, olive and brown ochres and the white kaolin from the rocks around them, and mixed the powder colours with water, milk or acacia gum.

Their great pastoral civilization lasted a long time, but overgrazing by the herds helped destroy much of the grass cover and so undermined the basis of life.

In this pastoral scene from over 3,000 years ago, women cook or chat and children play beside a hut drawn in section to show its contents.

Hunting for Sport or Survival

Paintings from the golden age of the Sahara show that the cattle-herding people hunted gazelle, antelope, giraffe and *mouflon*. They were armed with bows and arrows and used dogs to track and bring down prey. They also hunted hippopotamus in the rivers and the curved lines (left) may represent canoes.

Later on, as the Sahara became drier and could no longer support the large cattle herds, hunting became less a sport and more a vital search for food. In the rock paintings, cattle disappear by about 1000 B.C., when horses were introduced and, as if to reflect the increasing harshness, the style of Saharan art becomes stiffer, less detailed and less colourful (right).

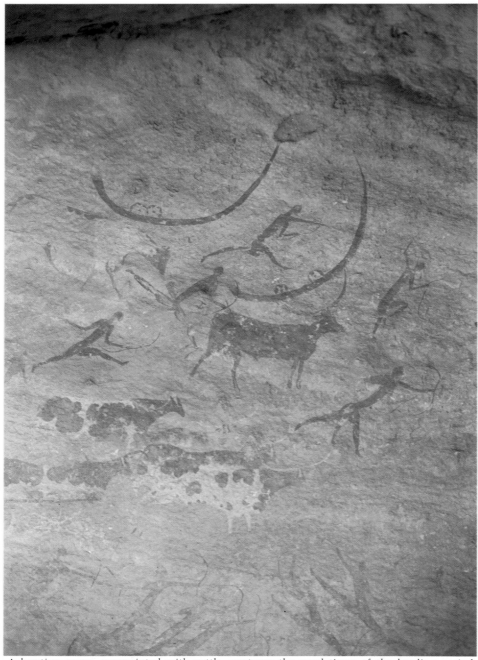

A hunting scene, overpainted with cattle, captures the good times of the herding period.

A hunter and his dog follow a trail.

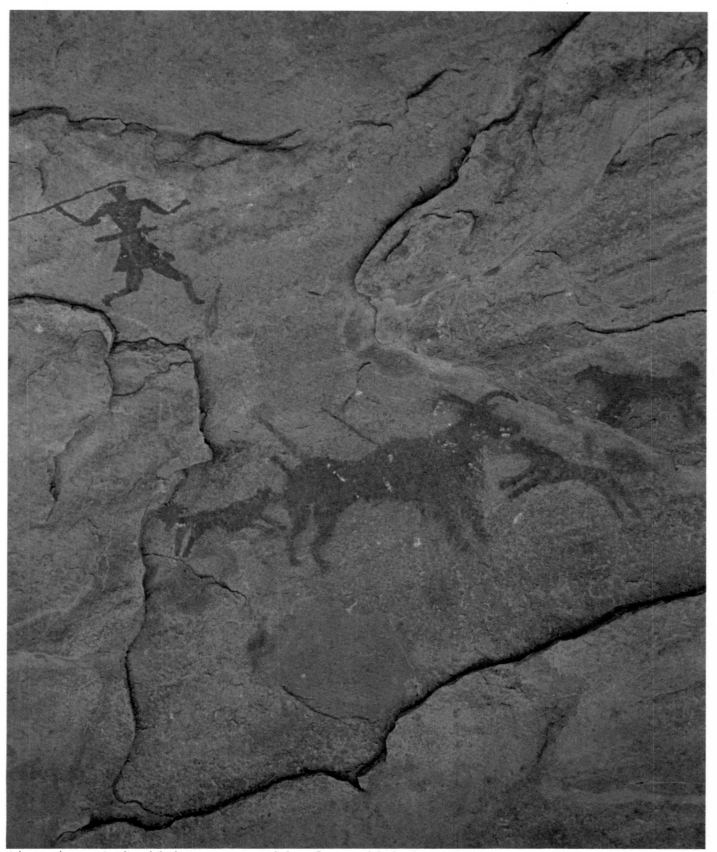

A hunter throws a javelin while dogs corner a wounded mouflon, one of the hardy animals that survived in the increasingly harsh Sahara.

NATURE WALK /Across the Tassili Plateau

It was still dark as we waited for the donkeys, and the October air was cold. I was about to start a ten-day walk in the Tassili n Ajjer mountains with photographer Pierre Boulat looking for flowers and animals, in particular for wild Barbary sheep, known in the Sahara as *mouflon*. These magnificent beasts have huge horns curving back to their shoulders and an apron of long hair that hangs from their throat and chest. They live in the remotest parts of the Tassili, and their agility and keen eyesight and hearing make them difficult to find.

We had driven early that morning from the oasis village of Djanet to the foot of the Tassili plateau; from here the baggage would have to be carried by the donkeys that Moussa ag Jebrin, our Tuareg guide, had arranged for us.

The lightening of the sky revealed a chaotic landscape. Huge conical heaps of debris stretched away on either side and, in front of us, the cliff rose sharply and cleanly from this rubble. The skyline of the plateau above remained black, but its crest, a long straight line broken by rock towers and pinnacles, was lit indistinctly from behind.

In a crevice in the rocks a small acacia thorn tree was growing, almost the only sign of life. There must have been a little rain in the past month, because there were minute green leaves at the base of each of the thorns which dotted the branches. But the thorns gave the tree little protection: all the lower branches had been heavily browsed by goats.

A 2,000-Foot Climb

The donkeys arrived shortly after sunrise, under the command of five donkey boys. Our baggage was loaded and we were soon heading up the track between the jumbled boulders. Our morning's objective was to reach the roof of the Tassili plateau over 2,000 feet above. We scrambled up the ancient bed of a mountain torrent, now dry and filled with slabs of sandstone. In the past a powerful river must have poured out here into the plains beneath, eroding the plateau and carrying away the debris. The cliff had been cut away by the force of this water, so that although the bed of the ravine was broad, the cliffs of red and maroon sandstone loomed over the track on either side, cutting out all but a narrow ribbon of sky. Little sun would

penetrate here, even at midday.

The first cliff took an hour to climb, and by the time we came out on a small plateau the donkeys had already fallen some way behind. There were scattered thorn trees and bushes growing in a thin layer of sand; gazelle tracks going from bush to bush indicated that animal life

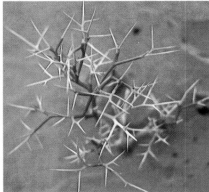

ACACIA THORNS

was more abundant than the silent emptiness suggested. A line of evenly spaced rock columns ran down the eastern side of the plateau, and the sun shining through them made a zebra pattern of black and white shadows on the sand. It was warm by now in the sun, but in the shadows it was still cold.

Pierre and I settled down with Moussa to wait for the donkey train. Moussa was tall and slim like most Tuareg, and was dressed in baggy green trousers tied at the waist with a decorated leather cord, and a flowing, blue, cloak-like *gandura*. Under this he wore, less traditionally, a striped nylon shirt and a pair of black rubber sandals

CRUMBLING SANDSTONE CLIFFS AT THE EDGE OF THE PLATEAU

made from lorry tyres. His face was covered in Tuareg fashion with a veil made of several yards of white muslin wrapped round half a dozen times. Only his eyes, and a few plaited tresses of black hair on the top of his head, showed.

I asked Moussa about the *mouflon*. "They are difficult to find," he said, "but perhaps we shall be lucky."

"Are there many of them?"

"There used to be lots, but they have been hunted too much. Now they hide. They have very good hearing and run away when people come."

As we talked, the little caravan came into sight. One of the donkeys had a water skin slung underneath its belly, a reserve in case we did not reach the water-hole at the top of the plateau before nightfall.

A Crumbling Cliff Face

A pile of scree and debris marked the beginning of the second cliff. The rock surface here was more exposed to the sun and darker, but fragments had fallen away, exposing the pale colours of the stone beneath. The path went directly up the cliff face and the donkeys with their bulky loads began to find the going difficult: occasionally one slipped on the loose rocks, or had to be helped over a tricky passage. The cliff became so steep that we had to scramble from rock to rock grabbing for hand and footholds.

For nearly an hour we climbed this steep face, pausing frequently for breath, and then suddenly we were at the top. Behind and far below, the foot of the mountain con-

WATER-ERODED RAVINE

trasted sharply with the white sand stretching west towards Djanet. In front of us was the plateau, an almost flat rocky pavement with a shiny black surface. This blackness gave the plateau a burnt-out look, as though the whole edifice had been baked too long in some gigantic geological oven.

We sat on the warm rock to get our breath back. Moussa pointed out the landmarks that were visible from our position on the edge of the plateau. As we talked, an isabelline-coloured lizard ran from the rocks to the sand in front of us. Not the least bit afraid, it stood with its nose in the air, watching.

We walked some miles across the plateau roof to get to our first camp site. We were so high, and the plateau so flat, that it was possible to see for miles around. In some of the shallow depressions in the rock pavement a little sand had gathered, and stunted bushes were struggling to grow. As we approached one of these, a hare with black ear tips broke cover and raced off across the rock, leaving a neat depression scraped in the sand under the bush.

The midday heat on the top of the plateau was stifling, and I was thankful when we reached a place called Tamrit where we were to camp for the first two nights. Here the flat rock gave way to a broad valley with vertical walls, worn back by the force of the water. But some blocks of rock had been left behind as the valley wall was eroded away, and they had caught the full force of the water. They were worn

FRINGE-TOED LIZARD

into a forest of thin aerodynamic shapes for which exotic similes sprang to mind: skyscrapers, ocean-liners, cathedrals, sharks' fins, or wine glasses. But none of these images did justice to the effects of a few million years of water and weathering on the soft sandstone.

The rocks were quiet, and at first the only sign of life was a cluster of small puff balls growing in the sand. But then I saw a party of brown-necked ravens sitting on the cliff above; they were waiting for us to be gone before they continued their meal on the carcass of a donkey that had died some time ago.

The rock formations dominated the landscape. It was a wild, crumbling place, well described by its Tuareg name—"plateau of rivers"—although the rivers here

CLUSTER OF PUFF BALLS

FOOD FOR SCAVENGERS

had been dry for thousands of years.

Or almost dry. In fact, a little of the water that had worked the landscape into shape was left, in a chain of small pools hidden in crevices between the rock columns. We were hot and thirsty from climbing in the heat, and these *gueltas*, dark green in the shade of the overhanging rocks, were a welcome sight.

There was a slight green scum on the surface of the water which had to be drawn aside before filling a mug or drinking with cupped hands, but during the two days we were here we drank the water, hesitantly at first, and then with pleasure when we discovered that it was clean and that the small red larvae swimming in it were harmless.

Painted Lady Butterfly

We were not alone in using this water. The sand bank of the *guelta* was marked with the footprints of the birds and small animals which had drunk there. A Painted Lady butterfly was gliding among the boulders, swooping low over the water from time to time. I sat on a rock overlooking the *guelta*, with my back against another rock, and waited to see whether any birds or animals would show up. The silence was eerie; down among the rocks there was not even the noise of wind. And the rocks effectively cut out any noise from Moussa and the others only 50 yards away. The calm was eventually broken by the staccato chattering of sandgrouse flying high overhead in V-shaped formation. They were probably arriving to

GUELTA HIDDEN IN THE ROCKS

PALE CRAG MARTIN

drink at this *guelta*, but seeing me they wheeled twice at a distance, and then disappeared.

A pair of pale crag martins was circling another, smaller *guelta* further down the chain and with binoculars I watched them bank and turn in perfect control of the complicated pattern of air currents set up by the hot exposed rock warming the cooler air above the pool. On the cliff face I could make out a cup-shaped saliva-and-mud nest. If the crag martins were breeding here it meant that they had found a regular source of food among the insects which were living at the *guelta* and that a short food chain was keeping an oasis of life going in the hostile plateau. Perhaps somewhere there was even a falcon feeding on the crag martins.

Plants were using the moisture too, and there were survivals here of Mediterranean species, strangely out of place thousands of miles from a Mediterranean climate. At the head of the *gueltas* was a large oleander,

which had formed a green bush covered with pink flowers; it was a shock to discover this splash of irreverent colour among the grey rocks. Though rooted in wet sand, the oleander had had to force a way up through the boulders that filled the rock fissure where it was growing. Moussa told us that the camels of the local Tuareg would not eat the oleander leaves, because they knew them to be poisonous, but camels brought here from beyond the Tas-

sili did not know this and often made themselves ill.

By the time I had taken a first quick look at this secret world around the *gueltas*, our caravan had caught up with us again. The donkeys were unloaded, then hobbled with short ropes and sent off to graze and drink at the *guelta*, and we set about making camp. I chose a shallow cave scooped in the rock face to give some protection from the night cold, and built a low wall of stones to make a wind-break.

As darkness spread across the landscape, we gathered firewood, and by nightfall had a fire blazing. Moussa and the donkey boys huddled around it, each wrapped in a blanket. As we talked after supper there was a hoarse croak above us and a heron flew over in the dark towards the south, outlined against the Milky Way. It must have been migrating from the north to spend the winter in tropical Africa, passing over the dry wastes of the Sahara as quickly as possible. "A night bird,

OLEANDER AT THE EDGE OF THE GUELTA

CYPRESS GROVE

evil spirit,'' said Moussa.

Moussa had told me that a few hundred yards from our camp there was a valley full of *tarout*, the cypress trees that are one of the Sahara's most curious Mediterranean survivals, so I made my way there early the following morning.

Entering through a narrow passage between two overhanging rocks, I found myself in a broad valley with a white sand floor, cut about 100 feet below the plateau top. It was closed at each end, and was entirely screened from the wind. The cliffs on either side protected the valley floor

from prolonged exposure to the sun at the height of summer, without keeping it permanently in the shade. The valley would also collect rain water from the surrounding plateau. It was an ideal place for Mediterranean plants struggling to survive in the Sahara.

The cypresses—about 15 of them —were tired old trees, in the wrong place and the wrong millennium. but they were magnificent. The oldest ones were hugely squat, 50 feet tall, and with a girth as much as half their height. The trunks twisted and turned like corkscrews.

Some were so gnarled that each tree seemed to be made of several different trunks growing from a single set of roots. At ten or 20 feet the trunks separated to form thick main branches running horizontally or even dipping again towards the ground. The bark had been shredded by hundreds of years' exposure.

The roots of the trees ran like tangles of thick cables over the rock, searching for a crevice, and some of them stretched 20 yards across the valley floor. The twisted shapes of the bark and exposed roots seemed to mirror the surrounding rocks as though thousands of years of shared weathering had brought wood and stone together—the trees, still alive but half-way to fossilization, and the rocks so twisted and sculpted by the water as to look almost alive.

Solitary Wheatear

A white-crowned black wheatear was the only other inhabitant of the valley that morning. It perched on a tangle of cypress roots watching me for a while, then went back to feeding. From time to time it made little hunting sorties, catching insects with a great snap of its beak in mid-flight. I moved slightly, and it turned its head to watch me curiously, without fear. I took a step and it flew, alighting on a small bush covered with spiky, double-headed fruit. The bush looked like a tiny cactus, with a thick skin to resist intense heat and dehydration. This was *Pergularia daemia*, a milkweed reputed to be poisonous.

PERGULARIA DAEMIA, A MILKWEED

I had asked Moussa to show us some of the prehistoric rock paintings for which the Tassili is famous, and later that morning he led us along a zig-zag path among the boulders and down to a large rock shelter that stretched several yards into the foot of the cliff.

On the sloping roof was a large and carefully drawn *mouflon*, with the characteristic huge horns curving back. It was painted in dark olive green, and the horns, delicately crosshatched, were exaggerated to give weight and emphasis to the animal—it was alert and wary, leaning forward expectantly and a little aggressively.

The *mouflon* seemed to have been held in awe. Indeed all the Tuareg still treat the wild sheep with respect: successful *mouflon* hunters are thought superior to other hunters, and the tents of important chiefs are made from their skins.

I began to understand why it was going to be so difficult to see these sheep on the plateau. If the *mouflon* of the Tassili had thousands of years' practice in escaping from Tuareg hunters, they would have little difficulty in avoiding two clumsy Europeans.

We spent three days exploring the rock paintings and arrived the fourth day at another group of small *gueltas*

WHITE-CROWNED BLACK WHEATEAR ON CYPRESS ROOTS

PREHISTORIC PAINTING OF MOUFLON

LIZARD TRACKS AROUND HELIOTROPE

SCORPION ON THE DEFENSIVE

the unreal landscape through rocky mazes, under arches, up crevices and along narrow passages, even coming out at one moment on to the flat top of the plateau, which stretched away, a rough rock pavement, to the edge of the Tassili cliffs. I tried hard not to step on loose rocks so as to make no noise, but I jumped back regardless when a large black scorpion appeared from beneath a boulder, its tail arched defensively over its head. It scuttled off into a crack in the rock wall.

The rock corridor we were following broadened out into a sandy arena scattered with bushes and we cast around for fresh tracks without success. Another corridor led away the other side and we followed it. After half an hour of this silent procession, Moussa found a place where the sandy floor of the valley was churned up. *Mouflon* tracks led away from the disturbed sand; their outline was razor-sharp, indicating that they were very fresh. Moussa beckoned to me and whispered: "*Udad* (*mouflon*) slept here last night."

We followed the tracks, alert and excited by the thought that the

surrounded with oleanders. In the sand around the camp site were signs of life: lizard tracks with the drag marks of their tails and, more importantly for our purpose, fresh hoof prints and droppings of *mouflon*. I asked Moussa whether we might not have a chance of seeing the sheep early next morning.

"This is not a good place," he said.

"But those tracks are fresh. It looks as though several have been here recently."

"They have probably gone now. There is some wind this evening and they will have smelt our camp fire."

Disregarding Moussa's hesitation, we set out on a sheep hunt in the dark, early the following morning. By first light we were tiptoeing in

ROOF OF THE TASSILI PLATEAU

A MAZE OF ROCK COLUMNS ON THE EDGE OF THE PLATEAU

animals were somewhere close to us in this rocky maze. The *mouflon* had made leisurely progress up the valley, stopping from time to time to browse on a small bush. In one place the sand was still dark and wet where the *mouflon* had urinated, and there were lots of small black oval pellets. Our *mouflon's* tracks were joined by others, and there seemed to be a small party moving together. Moussa followed the tracks easily across the sand, where they were obvious, and then over bare rock, where I could see no trace at all. He was obviously excited by the hunt, and his normal slow shuffle had become a fast walk, his rubber sandals making no noise on the rock.

A light breeze was blowing, and I remembered that we should try to be downwind from the animals we were pursuing. But the rock cliffs gave us no choice, and we had to follow the tracks wherever they went. Indeed, after a time it began to look as though the *mouflon* were making sure they stayed downwind of us. And then, in a patch of soft sand at the head of a small valley, the tracks were suddenly much deeper and closer together. Moussa looked at them for a moment and shook his head.

"They must have smelt us here and run off. We will not catch them now."

We turned back towards camp, disappointed by our lack of success, but consoled by the thought that there obviously were *mouflon* here to be seen if our luck and Moussa's skill were good enough.

But now the animals had escaped, Moussa's enthusiasm disappeared, and he became pessimistic about our chances again. It began to be irritating, since *mouflon* were the main object of our expedition. It was also surprising, since he was cheerful and optimistic about everything else.

A Forest of Rock Pillars

During the next two days we explored the roof of the plateau. From the top the view was sometimes spectacular; in one place we came out on to a flat rock terrace where we could see 30 or 40 miles to the east, through a forest of rock pillars to the sand dunes of Libya beyond.

The next day we started early on a long trip to the south-western side of the plateau. Several days in the Tassili had made it easier to see some order in what had at first seemed a formless jumble of rocks. The main body of the plateau had been weathered to a smooth flat surface, cut here and there by deep valleys and canyons. Later depositions of sandstone on the top of the plateau had left traces in the form of heavily eroded rock columns standing isolated on the rock pavement.

There were occasional sandy patches, and as we crossed one of them Moussa paused over a mark on the ground. With a warning sign of his arm that we should hold back, he cast around for a few moments and then pointed to the shadowy area under a small rock. I looked at the sand and saw a tell-tale series of S-shape furrows made by a horned viper. The snake was almost completely buried, resting or waiting in ambush for a careless rodent, lizard or bird, and only a small part of its head was visible. But the outline of its body was discernible from the

ERODED ROCK COLUMNS ON THE PLATEAU ROOF

pattern in the sand—short and thick and compressed into a tight concertina spring. Moussa, with a hatred of snakes understandable in one who walks nearly barefoot in a region where snakes are common, darted forward with his stick and pinned the viper to the ground by the back of its neck. The snake writhed, raising its buff body with dusty black markings clear out of the sand. Its mouth opened almost

180° as it struggled, showing large backward-pointing teeth. I normally like snakes, but there was something powerfully sinister about this viper, one of the most poisonous snakes in the desert. Moussa quickly killed it with a stone.

We reached Jabbaren in the late afternoon. Among the rocks there was a rich carpet of grasses, and several bar-tailed desert larks flew up as we passed. They and the wheatears were the only small birds able to find enough food to live in appreciable numbers on the plateau.

That night I tackled Moussa again on the subject of *mouflon*. We had seen lots of fresh tracks and I pointed this out to Moussa, saying that I was sure we would be able to see them if we really tried.

"It's very difficult. They will hear us from a long way off. Probably they have already left this area now that we are here."

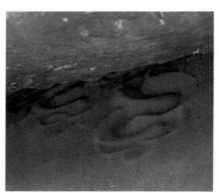
VIPER HIDDEN IN THE SAND

BAR-TAILED DESERT LARK

"But if we get up very early, we can search for them several hours away from here."

"I tell you, I do not think we will see them."

Moussa's pessimism was infuriating, and it seemed to be without any justification. Perhaps there was some other reason why he was being so cagey?

I began to think of other Saharan hunting expeditions I had been on, and then I remembered some days I had spent a year previously with the Nemadi of Mauritania. These people, who live mainly by hunting addax antelope in the remotest parts of the

SAND BLOWN AGAINST ROCKS

western Sahara, have elaborate rules of behaviour concerning their prey; in particular they go to some lengths to conceal their intentions.

The evening before the Nemadi go hunting, they do not talk about it, in case the spirits warn the addax. The Tuareg themselves—and I kicked myself for not remembering such an important fact—take similar precautions when they hunt *mouflon*. I was clearly being grossly insensitive in pressing Moussa.

I changed tactics at once. "No, perhaps you are right. It doesn't matter very much if we don't see them."

Moussa's face cleared, and for the first time since the discussion had started he looked straight at me. "You know," he said, "nobody here has seen a *mouflon* for a long time."

This was transparently untrue, but I was beginning to get the hang of it. I went on: "Anyway, even if we did see them, they would probably be too far away to take photographs."

"Probably."

There was a silence, and then we talked about other things for a few minutes before going to sleep.

Mouflon Tracks in the Sand

Pierre Boulat and I were awake the next morning before it was light, but when we got up Moussa was ready. Without a word we set off through the rock passages, Moussa shuffling silently ahead. As the sun rose we passed a small sand mound that had piled up against the rock wall of a passage. Its surface was rippled by the wind, and it glowed orange in the morning light.

Soon we had left the Jabbaren

MOUFLON TRACKS AND DROPPINGS

PLANT GRAZED BY MOUFLON

rocks behind, and were out again on the open plateau. After two hours' walking we were standing above a precipitous ravine. In the rocks was a small *guelta*, and the sand around it was marked with fresh *mouflon* tracks and droppings. The leaves of a crocus-like plant had been grazed by the same animals. *Mouflon* could not be far away.

Moussa approached the ravine cautiously, shielding himself behind a large rock outcrop. When he reached it he carefully removed his conspicuous white veil, and peered round the side of the rock. A moment later he turned back, his unveiled face jubilant. He beckoned us to approach with care, and pointed to the far side of the ravine.

"*Udad*," he whispered in my ear. "On the white sand."

I searched with the binoculars. There was some white sand on the opposite cliff face, and patches of green vegetation on it. There were also several indistinct brown shapes. I watched them for a moment and saw one of them move. It was a party of *mouflon*.

Moussa removed his sandals and motioned to us to take off our boots. The rock was warm under my feet as we set off down into the ravine, keeping out of sight in small gullies and crevices. In about 20 minutes

we came out on a terrace that looked directly across the ravine. I crept behind a small pile of boulders, while Moussa and Pierre continued in the hope of getting closer for photographs. Alone and flat on my stomach, I focused my binoculars on the white sand.

The End of the Search

There were five *mouflon* feeding peacefully on the recently greened bushes. They looked like heavy goats, standing more than three feet high, with warm honey-brown coats. The party was led by a large old ram with a lugubrious face and huge curved horns. He had a shrewdly suspicious look, and he paused occasionally in his browsing, standing immobile with his head lowered threateningly. A thick apron of shaggy brown hair grew from his throat down to his knees, and hung almost to the ground. This alder-

manic garment was entirely suited to his position in the little group, which was made up of three ewes and a lamb half the size of the adults.

The ram found a dust patch, and putting his head down, rubbed his jaw in it. Satisfied, he sank to the ground and wallowed luxuriously for a few moments, while the ewes waited their turn. When he had finished they each did the same, while the young lamb rushed playfully around the neighbouring rocks. Then they rested, sitting with all four feet tucked neatly under their bodies and chewed meditatively.

The *mouflon* slowly moved down the ravine towards the cliff, probably returning to a safe refuge in the rocks where they would rest during the heat of the day. At the last moment they suddenly scented danger and the ram's head came up sharply. Moussa and Pierre had got too close to them and Pierre was only able to get one quick photograph as the wild sheep raced off down the rocks.

Later that day we moved camp for the last time to the top of the Aroum col. Here the Tassili collapsed in a series of cliffs down into the white sand sea nearly 3,000 feet below. At its foot, isolated cones of debris formed an archipelago of black islands stretching out into the erg where small dunes were linked up in chains reaching towards huge sand pyramids. The horizon was hidden in an indistinct haze, into which the evening sun sank gently.

Early the next morning we climbed down the pass, and found the Land Rover waiting for us in the sand.

ESCAPING MOUFLON

ADMER ERG FROM THE TASSILI PLATEAU

3/ Seas of Wind-Patterned Sand

*The observer never fails to be amazed at a simplicity of form,
an exactitude of repetition and a geometric order unknown in
nature on a scale larger than that of a crystalline structure.*

RALPH BAGNOLD/ *THE PHYSICS OF BLOWN SAND AND DESERT DUNES*

The wind had been blowing fitfully from the north-east all day, but in the late afternoon it dropped for half an hour and then unexpectedly picked up again from the south, where black clouds began to pile up. I was living with Tuareg nomads on the southern edge of the desert and we were waiting for the dramatic dust storms that would announce the start of the brief summer rains; they were late this year and no one knew how much longer the wretched pasture could support the camels. At around six the clouds took on a rosy tinge, and re-formed into a mass lower and denser than before, which began to move towards the edge of the wadi where I was camped. The colours darkened to yellow, then red, until it seemed as though a huge mountain swathed in cloud was advancing towards us.

As it approached I could make out great eddies and whirls within it, and thick columns of dust were lifted hundreds of feet into the air by the violent wind. In the nomad camp there was much commotion; everyone was running to peg the tents down and herd together the goats browsing in the wadi. Hoping to get a good view of the storm, I gathered up my Tuareg face veil and set off for some high ground behind the camp. It began to thunder, not with single claps, but with a slow, indistinct murmur that quickly grew into a continuous angry rumbling all around the horizon. The swirling columns of dust now looked like a thick orange theatre curtain four miles across and 3,000 feet high, sweeping purposefully towards our wadi. A gust of wind tossed the thorn trees and almost tore the long veil from my fingers as I tried to wrap it round my face before the storm enveloped me. I was just in time.

The curtain of dust and sand swept through the camp, blotting out daylight in an instant. In the pitch dark, I had to crouch in order not to be blown over by the force of the wind. After a minute the dark was replaced by a dim orange glow. A few yards away, a Tuareg was trying to drag his camel to shelter, but the frightened beast, roaring and bellowing with its head down, refused to move. All over the camp there was a chorus of bleats and groans from animals unnerved by the storm.

There was clearly no sense in being outside so I made my way back to the camp, guided through the orange fog by the noise of the animals. My leather tent, normally open all round to let the air circulate, was firmly pegged down to the ground, but it gave little protection from the sand, which forced its way under the flaps and covered everything inside.

I had not been in the tent more than a few minutes when the rain started. At first it came in handfuls, drumming on the leather like hail. The tent was battered alternately by rain and sand; the rain dripped through the seams and sprayed under the flapping edges. I covered my papers as best I could, and settled down to sit out the storm. In about 20 minutes it was all over. The wind stopped abruptly, and the orange fog rolled away, leaving in its wake a silvery mist of floating dust which quickly cleared in the light drizzle that replaced the rain.

As the storm moved on, the camp came back to life. People emerged from battened-down tents, pulling their goats out after them. Naked children, shrieking with delight, splashed from one puddle of rainwater to another, making the most of this unexpected joy. Three bedraggled shepherds who had not been able to find shelter in time arrived in sodden veils and cloaks, and provoked roars of laughter from the men.

The rain had brought out the colours previously hidden by the dust and heat of the summer. The bark of the thorn trees in the wadi glowed a rich brown and the wet Tuareg tents recovered the red of the dyed leather. Even the black rocks behind the camp glistened brilliantly. The air was clear and free of the heaviness of the past week, but it was still hot enough to evaporate the puddles rapidly. Birds reappeared and got back to the business of singing, fighting, and posting the new territories that would be essential for nesting now that the rains had begun.

The rumble of thunder continued all evening as the storm moved round the mountains of the Adrar n Iforas a few miles away, and after dark the intricate tracery of lightning lit the whole horizon. In the south an electric storm gave an impressive display of pyrotechnics: lightning darted here and there in the clouds, constantly flickering and changing direction. Sometimes half a dozen flashes sprang from the same point, scattering across the sky like mercury. To the north the storm could still be seen, with thick red flashes striking again and again from the clouds to the ground. Later, when the storm had gone, a full moon rose. But it was veiled by dust and surrounded by Saturnal rings.

Violent storms such as this figure prominently in the mythology of the Sahara. There are many legends of lost oases and caravans or even armies buried in the sand. Herodotus left an account of a Persian army that set out to conquer the people of the Siwa Oasis in the Libyan Desert, but never arrived—when the soldiers were half-way there, a southerly wind "of extreme violence" blew up and they disappeared forever. Although that story may be apocryphal, a storm near El Oued in 1947 killed nearly 4,000 sheep and goats. And the wind can certainly carry dust long distances: after a storm in the Algerian Sahara in March 1947, reddish dust fell in the Swiss Alps, turning the snow pink.

But these brief, spectacular storms are less important in the long-term shaping of the sand landscape than a phenomenon called a sand wind, which occurs when a constant but only medium-strong wind is blowing. A sand wind is an eerie experience. The sand moves in a dense layer three or four feet thick, flowing steadily like a shallow, dirty river. On a camel or in a Land Rover you are often above this layer, bothered by no more than a little fine dust. I have eaten lunch quite comfortably standing up with a sand wind swirling around my legs. But it is a different story if you have to sleep in the dunes at night while such a wind is blowing. Your hair, nose and eyes fill with sand, as does your sleeping bag, even though you turn away from the wind and draw the hood as tightly as you can.

This moving carpet of sand is the main mechanism in the creation of the variety of sand-forms, ranging from tiny ripples to 1,000-foot hills, which make up the complex, shifting surface of the sand seas or *ergs*. A British army engineer, Ralph Bagnold, was the first to discover how the process works. In the 1930s he conducted a series of elegant experiments at Imperial College, London. He imitated a sand wind by blowing grains of different sizes down a wind tunnel and observed what happened. Under the influence of the wind, very small dust particles were lifted into suspension while medium-sized grains bounced along like balls hitting the ground at intervals. The harder the surface, the better the grains bounced. Bagnold called this saltation. Then he dis-

Ripples disturb the surface of a Saharan sand sea, or erg, with a hypnotic pattern of alternating crests and troughs. All sand formations are shaped and moved by the wind; but, as the next few pages show, they vary greatly in size, shape and mobility. Ripples like these, the smallest and fastest moving, are built up across the wind to a height of a few inches by the action of wind-driven grains bouncing along the surface of the erg.

covered that each time the medium-sized grains bounced they splashed more grains into the air and also pushed bigger ones—up to six times their own size—forward along the ground. So when the wind blows, the sand travels in three distinct layers: the lightest particles high in the air in suspension, the medium grains bouncing forward two or three yards at a time but rarely rising above six feet, and the heavy grains being pushed along the surface in what Bagnold called surface creep.

A continuous sand wind sorts the sand into ripples at right angles to the direction in which it is blowing. This happens because wherever there is a small irregularity, the surface creep falters and sand starts to pile up in a way that Bagnold compared to a traffic block. The ripple grows in height as coarse sand is pushed up the windward surface by the constant bombardment of bouncing grains, creeps over the crest and halts on the lee side, where it is sheltered from the wind and the impact of the bouncing grains. Meanwhile, the bouncing grains hitting the windward slope splash up and pass overhead. They fall the same distance downwind, because bouncing sand grains of any one size have a definite, measurable wavelength in any particular wind. Where the grains land, another ripple is formed which in turn creates a third, and so on. If the wind continues, the ripples move slowly forward as more sand creeps up over their crests and builds up new leeward faces in front of the old faces. The original coarse grains appear again on the windward slope as the ripple moves over them and creep up once more towards the crest. As the ripples advance, they keep the distance set for them by the force of the wind and the size of the grains.

For many years it was thought that dunes started life as ripples and simply grew. But although dunes are also formed by moving sand, the process is quite different. Small dunes are sometimes found in open gravel or pebble plains on the edge of sand seas, or even well away from them. The rough surface of these plains is usually filled with sand which has been deposited there when the wind drops. As the wind increases again the sand is lifted out and starts to travel in saltation, the grains bouncing well on the hard surface beneath. However, if they encounter a patch of sand collected in a hollow or behind a boulder, they immediately bounce less well and begin to accumulate in a heap. This is the birth of a dune. So long as the wind continues to bring sand, the dune will grow, until it reaches a height of about five to ten feet.

If the wind blows constantly from the same quarter, an isolated dune grows into the classic shape of a *barchan*, looking like a crescent moon lying on its side. Its arms stretch out downwind and a steep slip face is

Small dunes, like those shown on the left, stand five to ten feet high; they move more slowly than ripples, advancing ten to 20 yards every year. The simplest type of dune is the crescent-shaped barchan (top), which is formed by the action of a wind blowing constantly from one direction. A seif (bottom) is created when a seasonal wind from a new direction distorts the arms of a series of barchans to make one long, sculptured ridge.

formed (almost universally at an angle of 32°) on the inside of the crescent. The *barchan* is in constant motion. Sand is eroded from the windward slope and blown over the top, so the slip face becomes steeper until a small avalanche occurs, and sand slips down in front of the dune, taking it downwind a few inches each time. If there is an adequate supply of sand, new *barchans* are formed as the old ones move away, until there are groups of them neatly spaced and advancing together in a chain downwind. *Barchans* move about ten or 20 yards a year, although up to 50 yards has been recorded in Chad.

There is something rather unnerving about a landscape on the move, and the predatory manner in which *barchans* advance to block wadis and cut tracks. Ralph Bagnold felt it strongly. "In places," he wrote, "vast accumulations of sand weighing millions of tons move inexorably, in regular formation, over the surface of the country, growing, retaining their shape, even breeding, in a manner which, by its grotesque imitation of life, is vaguely disturbing to an imaginative mind."

If the wind is not constant, but blows sometimes from one quarter, sometimes from another, the crescent shape of the *barchan* is modified and a *seif* dune is formed. When the wind changes, one arm of the *barchan* begins to stretch downwind until it becomes a dune in its own right. Although the shape varies according to the wind patterns, all *seif* dunes have a single, continuous ridge with a crest that rises and falls in elegant, regular curves. This long, razor-thin ridge gives these dunes their name: *seif* is Arabic for sword. *Seif* dunes move erratically; although some are virtually static, others grow rapidly downwind.

When the *barchans* and *seifs* leave the hard flat areas and join a general mass of sand in an *erg*, they lose their distinct shape and move more slowly. Eventually they sort themselves into sinuous parallel lines a few hundred yards apart and a new pattern, known as *aklé*, emerges. From the air, *aklé* dunes look like the regular pattern of fish scales. They are the most dispiriting of all sand formations to cross: you painfully climb each line of dunes, dragging a laden camel behind you; and slither down a crumbling slip face only to start up towards the next crest.

Dominating the *ergs* are mountainous sand ridges known as *draa*, which are sometimes 1,000 feet high and lie in chains one to three miles apart. They are the creations of thousands of years of sand movement, dictated by wave-like wind patterns on a gigantic scale. *Draa* chains always have smaller sand formations on top, all moving downwind at their own speed: the *draa* chains themselves advance at the rate of an inch or two each year, the small dunes on top of them at several yards

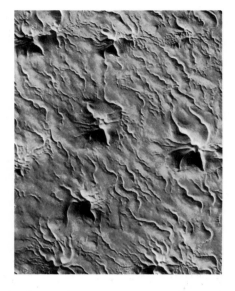

Ridges and mountains of sand, ribbed and cratered by the wind, create a moonscape effect in the centre of a great erg (right). Massive features of this type, several hundred feet high, dominate everything else in the ergs. The ridges, or draas, are laid out in great chains, generally at least a mile apart. Where draa chains cross, the winds create mountains called rhourds; these star-shaped formations are seen most effectively in isolation and from a height (above), in places where fully-fledged draas are absent.

a year, and the ripples on top of the dunes at a faster rate still.

Where two *draa* chains cross, star-shaped sand mountains, or *rhourds*, appear. In some *ergs*, perhaps the younger ones, *rhourds* and *draa* are heaped together without apparent sequence or order, with *barchans* and *seifs* between and *aklé* dunes on top of them adding to the confusion. But in other areas, like the southern part of the Erg Chech, individual *rhourds* and *draa* are spaced out in orderly fashion, separated from each other by large spaces of flat sand and gravel. In places this hard pavement forms corridors that run for miles in straight lines through parallel *draa* chains. One of the longest of these, the Gassi Touil, is several miles wide and cuts for 200 miles through the Great Eastern Erg in Algeria. For centuries it has been the link between the Arab north and Tuareg south. Nomad caravans followed it, as did the French soldiers who conquered the Sahara; more recently a tarmac road has been constructed in it for lorries servicing the oil wells in the middle of the desert.

To me, the sand seas are some of the most exciting of Saharan land-scapes. You can drive into them on hard corridors, or if you are feeling more adventurous and have the right equipment—a four-wheel drive vehicle with heavy-treaded sand tyres let down until they are very soft—you can set off over some of the dune surfaces. No one had tried to drive a vehicle over a dune until Ralph Bagnold showed that it could be done in 1929. While on an expedition into the Libyan Desert, Bagnold drove a lorry at a large dune at 40 m.p.h., "feeling like a small boy on a horse just about to take his first fence". The result was dramatic. "A huge glaring wall of yellow shot up high into the sky a yard in front of us. The lorry tipped violently backwards—and we rose as in a lift, smoothly, without vibration. We floated up and up on a yellow cloud. All the accustomed car movements had ceased; only the speedometer told us we were still moving fast. It was incredible. Instead of sticking deep in loose sand at the bottom as instinct and experience both foretold, we were now near the top, a hundred feet from the ground."

Bagnold's later experiments showed that the sand in large low dunes was packed by the action of the wind so densely that, although you could run your hand through it easily, it would bear the weight of a small lorry. With this discovery many new parts of the desert were opened to exploration by vehicle; Bagnold himself made use of the fact when he set up the Long Range Desert Group in World War II, and attacked behind the Italian lines in North Africa in areas which were thought impenetrable by vehicles. Of course it is impossible to drive a car on the sand mountains, or where the sand is moving fast and forms sheer crests. But in many areas of low sand hills and dunes you can drive a Land Rover more or less where you want. I spent three weeks one spring in Mauritania driving almost entirely on low rolling sand dunes, and it was an exhilarating experience.

In the early morning and evening the shadows thrown by the dunes made it easy to steer a course among the hollows and peaks. But in the middle of the day it became dangerous: in the blinding glare of the sun there were no shadows and no perspective. Without care I knew we might find ourselves driving straight over the top of a crest with a sharp drop on the other side. One day in the first week we nearly came to grief in this manner. My guide knew the area well by camel but had never been in a Land Rover before. We were trying to find a passage through a line of sand-obstructed cliffs where almost certainly no vehicle had ever been, and we had almost given up hope when we saw a long rise of hard sand ahead that seemed to skirt the rocks. Asking the guide and my companion to get out and walk for their own safety and to reduce weight, I drove the Land Rover at medium speed up the hill. The large sand tyres sank in slightly, but the vehicle kept going. I reached a crest and could not see what was beyond; I had the choice of stopping, which would mean losing the vehicle's valuable momentum and almost certainly getting stuck, or pressing on. I decided to play safe and stopped. When I got out to investigate I saw I had made the right decision. Beyond the crest the sand fell away for several hundred feet into a valley enclosed on all sides by sheer rock. Had I gone over the top, and still managed to keep the car from overturning and rolling down the slope, there would have been no possible way of getting it out of the valley, short of taking it apart and carrying out the bits by camel.

Another hazard of the Mauritanian dunes is quicksand. We were speeding along when suddenly the Land Rover stopped without warning, as if it had run into an invisible rubber wall. When we got out, we found it was axle-deep in soft sand, indistinguishable from the firm sand all around. These areas of soft sand probably mark the slip faces of old dunes. The theory is that in some circumstances, dune forms may be reduced over time to an undulating sand sheet where the original crests have been planed off, perhaps by wind blowing in a new direction. At the ancient slip faces, the sand lies in steeply sloping rather than horizontal layers, and can bear no weight.

The first time it happened was in the late afternoon. It would take several hours digging the vehicle out with a spade, placing sand ladders under the wheels and reversing back on to the hard sand, so I decided to camp for the night and leave the hard work until morning. In the isolation of the dunes the silence was complete, and our footsteps were muffled by the sand. Low dune crests surrounded us with sinuous and parabolic curves, each repeating the others' shape as though they had come from the same mould. Their surface was rippled with tiny ridges which the evening sun turned into an elusive pattern of light and shade. On the horizon some low *rhourds* made a jumble of ridges, peaks and valleys in which it was difficult to see a regular design. The connecting ridges snaked for a mile or two between the peaks, and on the lee of each side was a steep slip face three to four feet high, like a defensive wall built across a turbulent hill frontier. Sand blew off the summits of some of the *rhourds* and formed into tiny whirlwinds that rushed down the steep slopes into the valley below. It was easy to give these whirlwinds personalities or think of them as playful spirits.

In the other direction the sand flattened out into a hard gravel corridor, and there was a small cluster of *barchans*. Their neat yellow crescents stood out prominently against the black gravel, and their arms were all exactly aligned towards the south-west, which was to be expected since the prevailing wind was from the north-east. They were about 30 yards apart, but two had joined up, with a snaking crest from crescent to crescent. None was more than five feet high and on the windward side they sloped gently up from the surface of the gravel. When I stood among them and looked downwind, the shape of the dunes was almost invisible and the silhouettes of the crests merged into a uniform mass of sand, but when I turned and looked upwind, the deep shadows cast by the sheer faces of the lee sides made an impressive show. The surface of these *barchans* was rippled and in the evening sun they glittered like watered silk.

As I walked barefoot, taking possession of our hollow in the fading light, I could feel the textures of the sand beneath my feet. A small red dragonfly quartered one hollow, and a group of swallows flew over a crest, heading north for their summer territory. The evening air was cool, a reminder of the cold season just ending when the night temperature in the dunes would have approached freezing. Later, when the moon rose, the sand was as silvery as mountain snow.

That night, surrounded by sand, I wondered about one of the most extraordinary desert phenomena. In certain parts of the desert, on a still evening after a windy day, the dunes suddenly and spontaneously start to boom with a low but penetrating sound, loud enough to drown conversation nearby. The sound comes from the lower part of a sand avalanche as it flows down the slip face of a dune, so it can fairly be described as the sound of the dune moving forwards. Not all dunes make the sound; records of it are rare, and it only seems to happen in rather special circumstances.

Ralph Bagnold heard it, of course. He described it as "the great sound which in some remote places startles the silence of the desert. Native tales have woven it into fantasy; sometimes it is the song of the sirens who lure travellers to a waterless doom; sometimes it is said to come upwards from bells still tolling underground in a sand-engulfed monastery; or maybe it is merely the anger of the jinn! . . . I have heard it in south-western Egypt 300 miles from the nearest habitation. On two occasions it happened on a still night, suddenly—a vibrant booming so loud that I had to shout to be heard by my companion. Soon other sources, set going by the disturbance, joined their music to the first, with so close a note that a slow beat was clearly recognised. This weird chorus went on for more than five minutes continuously before silence returned and the ground ceased to tremble." But that night—for me— the dunes remained silent.

In the morning we dug the vehicle out and continued north across the Mauritanian sands.

Into the Unknown Sahara

The Sahara is a forbidding place, even to the visitor with modern maps, medicines and vehicles. It was a great deal more hazardous for the first Europeans who set out to cross its vast wastes: from the ill-fated Scotsman Major Gordon Laing, who was murdered near Timbuktu in 1826, to Heinrich Barth, the German linguist, historian and geographer, who in the 1850s raised Saharan exploration to a new level of scientific precision.

These pioneers had little idea of what to expect. The geographic information available—culled from such classical and Arab sources as Herodotus, Ptolemy and Leo Africanus—was generally inaccurate. The desert appeared on old maps as a fanciful landscape featuring mythological beasts and fabulous cities, echoes of the rich empires that rose and fell in sub-Saharan Africa. The most celebrated of these cities was Timbuktu, which was idealized as an El Dorado of the dunes. Many explorers were lured across the Sahara by the magic of the name, searching for a city of wealth and learning.

They were adventurous individuals, mainly from Britain, France and Germany, who represented the powerful, outward looking Europe of the 19th Century. Some, like Réné Caillé, plunged into the desert on their own initiative. Caillé set out from Senegal disguised as an Arab and finally reached Timbuktu in 1828. He was bitterly disappointed with what he found. After two weeks he turned north across the desert and became the first European to reveal that the fabulous city was, in fact, a town of mud.

Most of the explorers were sponsored by governments and learned societies. In 1819, Captain George Lyon (right) made a 1,400-mile journey from Tripoli to Tajarhi under the auspices of the British Government, which hoped to open up the African interior to trade.

Like many of his successors, Lyon suffered appallingly in the huge waterless tracts (which accounted for the lives of over 150 missionaries and explorers during the next century). He was continually weakened by dysentery, malaria and infections of the liver and kidneys. At one point he was bedridden for 22 days and his recovery, he wrote, was "looked on as a miracle".

Heavily shrouded against a swirling sandstorm, Captain George Lyon, an explorer who crossed the Sahara in 1819, drives his camel on towards the town of Tajarhi, while slaves left behind to die plead for water.

Vignettes From a Desert Diary

The eastern Sahara was first crossed by Europeans in 1822. The explorers, who travelled from Tripoli to Lake Chad, were a British trio: Dixon Denham, an army major, Hugh Clapperton, a naval lieutenant and the leader, Walter Oudney, a doctor.

Breaks from the daily tedium of sand and rock were recorded with special feeling. Once they encountered hundreds of bleached skeletons, the remains of slaves who had died on previous caravans. Denham noted with horror how his horse cracked the brittle bones underfoot and kicked a skull like a football.

At another time, wrote Oudney, "Clapperton . . . called out several times for me to dismount from my camel to enjoy the treat"—a deep valley with two fine lakes. The waters contained fly-larvae the size of rice grains. Reddish-brown and with a "strong slimey smell", the larvae were scooped up in handnets by wading villagers. When dry, the larvae were pounded with salt into a paste, ready for eating.

From time to time desert animals which were still little known in Europe caught the travellers' interest. Denham reported having caught "a small beautiful animal, nearly white, much resembling a fox in make and shape, although not larger than a moderate-sized cat". He had trapped a fennec, the smallest of foxes, adapted to the desert.

Hugh Clapperton, a brawny Scot, hunted with a North American Indian tribe and explored Labrador before journeying twice across the Sahara, where he met his death at the age of 39.

Major Dixon Denham, as this portrait suggests, saw himself as a Byronic figure. He was the expedition's diarist and complemented his narrative of the journey with accomplished sketches.

Denham sketched this tiny fennec fox, which he had managed to catch after a chase.

Like a polished medallion pinned to the desert floor, this lake near Ghat offered a refreshing respite from the monotonous aridity.

Heinrich Barth was the most scholarly and wide-ranging explorer of his time. He brought a classical education and a deep-rooted love of travel to his journals, but his leaden prose did not appeal to the public and few read them.

A Scholar's Encounter With the Wilderness

From the day Heinrich Barth left Tripoli in 1850 on his 10,000-mile journey to Timbuktu and Lake Chad, he zealously kept a full and accurate diary. His notes, which filled five heavy and indigestible volumes when published, became a valuable source for later explorers. He identified rock formations, described the terrain, vegetation, animal life, rock drawings and life and language of the desert peoples, and recorded three temperature readings daily.

Though his companions died of fever and exhaustion within the first year and though the nomads displayed a dangerous "cupidity and greediness for booty", his stoicism and strength of purpose never flagged. Once he was lost in the sand for two days with no water and only a leafless tree for shade. He eventually rescued, but not before his raging thirst had reduced him even to sucking his own blood.

This "picturesque valley Welad Ali" was once, according to Barth, adorned with orchards and groves of date-palms. The desolation portrayed here was a sign of the Sahara's increasing aridity, emphasized by the scene of a hyena and jackals picking away at a dead camel.

Lit by eerie moonlight, the mountains
of Hombori near Timbuktu soar
upwards like Gothic battlements in this
drawing by Heinrich Barth—who added
a whimsical touch by placing a lone
heron on the shore. For all his scientific
discipline, Barth had a romantic's
perception of grand landscapes.

4/ In the Shelter of the Dunes

*In the true desert not even jackals can survive; there are only
the addax and the fennec, which were made by God to remind
man of his own modest capabilities.*   SIDATI AG SHEIK, TUAREG CHIEF

After ten days' walking in the Tassili n Ajjer mountains, and encouraged
by our successful search for *mouflon*, I decided to make a short trip into
the Admer Erg nearby to look for addax, the rare antelope that is one of
the Saharan animals best adapted to desert conditions. The Admer Erg
used to be one of its strongholds.

A camel was the only possible form of transport if I was to explore
the dunes thoroughly and I found two Tuareg in Djanet who agreed to
come with me for a few days, bringing riding and baggage camels with
them. A trip by camel is an excellent way to see an *erg* and its plant and
animal life. A camel travels at a reasonable pace and in the saddle you
are high enough—six or seven feet off the ground depending on the size
of the animal—to have a. clear view all around. The muffled progress
of a camel party scarcely disturbs the peace of the dunes. We set off from
Djanet in the afternoon and were among the dunes two hours after we
had left the date palms of the oasis behind. The first evening we stopped
early and camped in a shallow hollow with sand crests snaking around us.

The next morning I had intended to make an early start as we had a
long day's journey in front of us. But it is difficult to hurry camels, and
even more difficult to hurry Tuareg who do not have urgent business of
their own. In our hollow there was no sign at all of the camels, whose
hobbles had not prevented them from wandering away among the dunes
in search of food, and the two indistinct shapes of the guides on the

ground, wrapped in blankets, showed no sign of movement. I packed my kit with as much noise as possible. Around seven the guides stirred. They rekindled the ashes of the previous evening's fire and made tea with the elaborate ritual that has great charm when you are being entertained at leisure, but is infuriatingly slow and mannered when you are waiting in the cold with a busy day ahead.

Tea drunk, the two men set off to follow the camels' tracks, but it was half an hour before they were back at the camp. Here the protesting animals were forced to crouch, rough saddle blankets made from old scraps of cloth were thrown over their backs and the saddles were put on and attached with girth ropes. The pack saddles were simple frames, and the baggage was loaded on both sides at once, to balance the weight, and attached by looped cords to the pommel of the saddle. The riding saddles were more elaborate: high-backed seats with a cruciform pommel in front, richly decorated in painted leather and brass.

When the camels were finally saddled and loaded, we set off across the dunes. For the first hour we walked, trailing the riding camels behind us by a single bridle rope. We crossed hollows and crests that succeeded each other regularly, until the dunes flattened out into a corridor of hard sand, and here we mounted and rode. We passed the day in this manner, alternately riding and walking. At six o'clock we found a series of dune hollows with adequate vegetation for pasture, and decided to stop there for the night. We made the camels crouch, unloaded and hobbled them, and sent them off to graze while we made camp. The men unrolled their blankets and made a fire, and I unpacked my kit.

I had learned on earlier Saharan trips that a few small luxuries are indispensable to nomad life. One of mine was a large red and black nomad carpet woven in a traditional design in the Mzab oases on the northern edge of the Sahara. In the desert you sit on the ground, and that usually means sand, rock or gravel which at night may be near freezing point. A thick carpet takes the edge off the hardness and cold. It is an expensive item for desert nomads, and is treated with some ceremony: you always kick off your sandals before walking on to one, and placing people on a carpet can be as delicate as deciding the seating plan around a conference table. To this traditional nomad luxury I had added two modern ones: an old camp bed, and a mountain sleeping-bag. The nomads sleep on the ground, but I have found it something to avoid whenever possible. It is hard and often cold, and at night alive with camel-spiders, scorpions and snakes. Scorpions in particular seem to like the warmth of a sleeping person and his bedding, and a Tuareg once told me laughingly of waking to find six scorpions curled in his blankets. Being a few inches off the ground does wonders for my peace of mind in such circumstances, although it would certainly disqualify me in the eyes of a Saharan of the old school. But the most rigorous purist could not object to my down sleeping bag, which is both lighter and warmer than blankets. The nomads themselves were clearly jealous of it.

During supper that night I questioned the Tuareg about our position. We were already about 40 miles into the erg. The scattered bushes our camels were feeding on were not rich enough to attract Tuareg flocks and we were not on any caravan route, so it seemed likely that the dune life here would be undisturbed.

Desert plants and animals are seen at their best in dunes like these, and the most curiously adapted species are found here. Although at the surface the sand can be heated by the sun to over 175°F, it is comparatively moist and cool further down. Rain that penetrates more than a foot is protected from re-evaporation and provides an opportunity for plants with long roots. The temperature is noticeably reduced even four inches below ground and at a depth of three feet remains steady day and night at a comfortable 75°F; numerous small animals take advantage of this fact and live in holes and burrows, where they are protected from the heat of summer days and the cold of winter nights alike.

As we finished eating, a camel-spider raced up to our camp fire as though to investigate this unexpected disturbance in the normally empty dunes. These ferocious looking animals—this one was five inches across—have two pairs of powerful jaws which they wave menacingly. They spend the day in burrows and come out at night to hunt insects and scorpions, or even lizards, mice and small birds. The male camel-spider uses his jaws not only for hunting but for mating. He immobilizes the female by stroking her and then holds her with one pair of jaws as he tucks a sperm capsule into her abdomen with the other pair. The sperm capsule, which scorpions also produce, is a useful device in the desert, where liquid sperm would be in danger of drying up.

I was up before sunrise the next morning, looking for tracks in the sand. On an adjacent dune a large bird—almost certainly a raven—had landed at a run, its tracks deeply dug in and well spaced. It had broken up some camel droppings in search for dung beetles, and had walked across the domed summit of the dune to watch our camp while we were still asleep. Then it had taken off again.

As I examined the footprints, a large ant with a silver body hurried past: presumably the silver would reflect the sun and protect the ant from the heat. I followed it down into a hollow, and then clambered up the soft sand of the ridge beyond. From the top, a movement in the next hollow caught my eye, and I sank down behind the crest with binoculars to watch. Two small fennec foxes were playing among the low bushes. They made quick delicate gestures, more like cats than foxes, and their pale isabelline coats and white faces were good camouflage against the sand. One of the fennecs played with a beetle, patting it backwards and forwards, and the other watched, its huge ears pricked and alive to the surrounding noises; fennecs are active mostly by night and, like many desert animals, rely on hearing more than sight. The fennec eventually ate the beetle, keeping its ears pinned back like a cat eating supper, and then the two of them settled down close together, lying head to tail, grooming each other. They rested like this for a moment, then one yawned and they both ran off over a ridge, moving fast on the soft sand.

This hollow was clearly an important centre of dune life. Every bush had several holes beneath it, probably belonging to lizards and small rodents. A highway of tracks joined up the most favoured tufts, some of which had been nibbled down to half an inch from the ground by gazelles and other visiting animals. The pad marks of a large carnivore, probably a sand fox, crossed the hollow and disappeared over the rim. A buff desert lark ran in front of me, and I noted its tracks for the future: they were shaped like a dagger, with a long blade made by the hind toe. There was a variety of plants in the hollow. Most conspicuous were the *had* plants (*Cornulaca monocantha*), compact round bushes with blue-green branches and small yellow thorns which are the staple fare of camels in remote dune regions. There were also tufts of *afozo*, (*Panicum turgidum*) a rank, unnourishing grass on which camels and wild animals have to fall back when all else fails. These hardly amounted to a rich pasture but when it had probably not rained for a year or more they were a surprising sight.

Both *had* and *afozo* belong to the category of plants that resist the desert heat and drought. Plants in this category have roots that either dig down to the moisture deep in the sand or spread horizontally to catch dew and surface water after rain, creating vast networks just beneath the surface of the sand: one such grass plant was found to have 50 miles of roots. The leaves of drought resisters are thick and small to cut down evaporation, or there may even be no leaves at all, in which case the branch or stalk takes over photosynthesis.

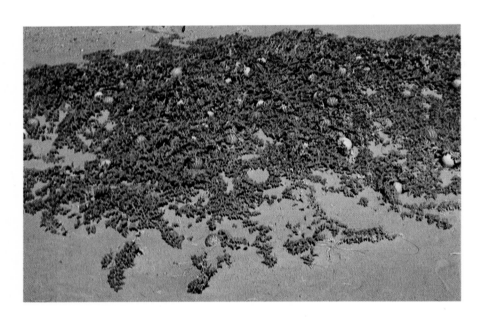

Wild colocynth melons ripen on the sand in a tangle of coarse leaves. When they are mature, the stems wither and the brittle, gourd-like fruits break off and roll away in the wind to new resting sites. In the heat of the sun they eventually burst open and expel their black seeds, which are ready to germinate when rain next falls.

Other plants avoid the problems of heat and drought altogether, by lying dormant in the sand as seeds or vegetative organs, waiting for a year or more before they grow and flower. When enough rain falls to trigger off the reproductive process, a race against time begins as the plants try to complete their breeding cycle before the moisture disappears. Almost all Saharan ephemeral flowers and grasses of this sort germinate within three days of adequate rainfall (by contrast, only six per cent of Scandinavian species do likewise), and many plants have sown their seeds within ten or 15 days of germination. White and violet crocus-like flowers, yellow desert daisies and other opportunists fight for every inch of ground and each small puddle until leaves and flowers of different species cover sandy hollows and wadi beds with the temporary carpet of vegetation known to nomads as *acheb*. These freshly greened patches attract gazelle, and camels meditatively chew mouthfuls of the gaudy flowers.

With rain so scarce, desert plants distribute their seeds as widely as possible to maximize their chances of catching a shower. On the southern edge of the Sahara, where seeds need to be carried against the prevailing north-easterly winds, many plants have barbed or spiked seed cases which catch easily in animals' coats. *Cram-cram* (*Cenchrus biflorus*), one of the spikiest of the grass seeds, is such a nuisance that most southern Tuareg and Moor nomads carry a small pair of tweezers to remove the thorns from their feet. Before setting up camp they have to brush the seeds away with a thorn branch to prevent them from hooking unyieldingly on to carpets and blankets.

In the central and northern desert, on the other hand, plants can use the north-east winds to blow their seeds, and sometimes even the whole uprooted plant, into new areas. One of the most spectacular of these wind-dependant plants is the wild Saharan colocynth melon, which grows in low rolling sand country. Each plant occupies a sandy mound and sends out tentacles which criss-cross and double back on each other to form a thick green mat, half-buried by sand. When the melons ripen they break loose and are free to be blown several miles by the wind. I have ridden through hard sand where hundreds of melons were scattered like small footballs without a parent plant in sight.

As I examined the plants, three swallows flew low over the sand ridge and briefly investigated the hollow for insects. In spring and autumn, swallows often feed among the dunes, particularly at dawn and dusk, unexpected reminders of the huge streams of migratory birds passing unseen high above. It has been estimated—and one can do no more than that—that around 5,000 million land birds from Europe and north and west Asia migrate to tropical Africa each winter, and a very large proportion of these cross the desert. They are surprisingly conservative in their choice of destination. If these swallows had come from Germany, they would be on their way to the Congo. If on the other hand they were among the million or two swallows that set out from Britain each year, they were probably going to South Africa, crossing the path of the German swallows on the way.

The journey is so long and severe that perhaps only half the migrating birds return to their nesting grounds in Europe the following spring. Small and apparently fragile warblers, nightingales, redstarts and wagtails, as well as a host of larger birds such as herons, ducks, terns and waders, have to cross Europe, then 500 miles of Mediterranean, followed immediately by 1,000 miles of Sahara. Some birds' journeys are unimaginably long. Two days before, I had seen a willow warbler in the date palms of Djanet. It could have come from Finland or Soviet Central Asia, and have been on its way to the West African coast or the Congo; in only five or six months it would have to set off on the return journey. Some willow warblers, shy, leaf-green birds four inches long, are known to fly from Siberia to South Africa and back—a distance of 7,500 miles each way—every year. The reason for this extraordinary journey is simple: it enables the birds to take advantage of the vast quantity of food available in summer in Europe and Asia. The birds, which probably began their migration over much shorter distances when the desert was smaller, must have learned to extend their journeys as the Sahara spread after the final retreat of the European ice-cap some 10,000 years ago.

Small birds fly at about 25 m.p.h., and with help from the prevailing north-easterly winds they make the Saharan crossing in about 40 hours of continuous flying. Most of them do not vary their course to follow greener areas like wadis, oases, mountain ranges—or even the Nile valley, as one might expect—but keep going on a broad front, heading straight for their destination. They have made their fat reserves before starting the journey, and the important thing for them is to finish it as swiftly as possible. The speed made by some birds is remarkable. A tiny sedge warbler, ringed in mid-April at Lake Chad, was found only a month later 150 miles beyond Moscow.

The sun had risen, and I walked back towards the camp between the dunes, crossing the bed of a shallow depression that was covered with a hard, white calcareous pavement. On the sand around it were signs of life—mollusc shells, fragments of pottery, bones and a small stone arrowhead. At some stage, presumably during the last wet period in the Sahara several thousand years ago, this depression had been a marsh or small lake, with camps of hunting and fishing people beside it. Then desert conditions returned and the lake dried up, leaving only a hard crust of residual salts. The people who lived here would have been driven away, possibly into the Tassili mountains to the east, where the climate remained less severe.

For dune-adapted animals, however, the hollows still offered a possibility for life. The scattered tufts of grass and bushes implied moisture, and in the early morning, the sand felt damp and cold through my open nomad sandals. Later in the day it would give protection to any creature that burrowed. But this is the only concession the dunes make to animal life. There are no luxuries here like the mountain *gueltas*, which provide water and food. In the *ergs* animals face the same problems as plants: how to avoid heat, and how to make do with very little water.

Few animals can stand direct exposure to the sun for very long: lizards, snakes and rodents all die within a few minutes if they are left on the surface of the sand without shade on a hot day. So dune animals avoid the surface, most commonly by burrowing down to the cooler, moister sand beneath. Camel-spiders even plug their holes with a wad of dead leaves to isolate the cool air inside from the hot air above. Some

In a gravel corridor between the dunes, the shade cast by an acacia offers a rare chance of shelter for an animal too large to burrow.

desert animals take a simpler approach. Certain lizards of the skink family live in the more clement layers of sand without bothering to excavate burrows. They have a wedge-shaped jaw for digging, eyes covered with transparent scales and smooth body scales; with this equipment they swim through the sand so easily that they are sometimes called sand fishes. Some desert beetles do even better. They feed at the slip face on the lee side of the dunes and, merely by making small digging movements with their legs, can start a small avalanche of sand which covers them from the sun. Most of the animals which live in burrows, like jerboas, and many of the predators that feed on them, like fennecs and sand foxes, are active mainly at night.

During the hottest season of the year, some otherwise diurnal animals become temporarily nocturnal; others—certain beetles for example—time their larval and pupal stages for these periods of intense heat. The most extreme way of avoiding the worst conditions is simply to go to sleep and wait for better times. Aestivation—the summer equivalent of hibernation—is rare among mammals, but some invertebrates can carry suspended animation very far. A desert snail which had been glued to a display card in the British Museum for four years revived after being put in water. Other snails collected in the desert after five years of drought, put in a jar and forgotten for another three and a half years, nevertheless came back to life when given water.

The true hallmark of dune animals is the ability to overcome an almost total lack of water, by finding liquid in food and then conserving it from evaporation, or even by doing without altogether. Many invertebrates, like beetles and scorpions, have a hard protective shield covering their bodies, and this effectively stops loss of water. Desert predators can generally get all the water they need from the body fluids of their prey. Saharan folklore recognizes this ability. A nomad proverb says: "Jackal tracks, water near. Fennec tracks, tighten your belt and keep walking." Jackals, like most savannah animals, have to drink regularly, whereas fennec and other carnivores of the desert delegate their problem by eating water-rich insects, lizards and rodents. Falcons and larks likewise get all their water ready-made from bird or insect prey.

Several non-predatory mammals, particularly those small enough to avoid the worst heat, also show considerable prowess in doing without water. Many desert rodents and gazelle do not worry about drinking, and for months on end get all their water from their food (the rodents from dry plants which contain almost none), and from oxidation water

An addax antelope pauses briefly during a meal of perennial grasses from which it derives both its food and water. This rare and highly-adapted desert animal seldom, if ever, drinks. It migrates long distances to find pasture, sometimes to the southern fringes of the Sahara where this photograph was taken.

they metabolize within their bodies. After rain, when there are pools of water in the dune hollows, they probably drink. But they do not need to; gerbils have lived in laboratories for several years without water.

The most spectacular example of adaptation to life without drinking is the addax antelope I hoped to see in the Admer Erg. Under normal conditions they never drink at all. Addax are four feet high at the shoulder, with a greyish white coat and magnificent black spiral horns. Somewhat heavy and cow-like when standing still, they can move for brief periods at a fast gallop over the soft sand, helped by broad hooves. Small herds of ten or 15 animals sometimes travel together, and a herd of 70 has been seen in the Mauritanian Majabat. Addax feed on perennial grass tufts and *had* bushes. They move many miles in search of this food and also undertake long-ranging seasonal migrations. In Chad at the end of the dry season when the Sahara is uniquely hostile to life, addax may migrate as far as the desert edge in search of pasture.

Addax were once widespread in the Sahara, and it is even possible that they were partly domesticated by the Egyptians. A stone carving records that Sabu, a priest of the sixth dynasty, owned 1,244 addax, and the carving shows them grazing peacefully under the watchful eye of a shepherd. But from the neolithic period onwards addax were harried by the joint effects of increasing dryness and human hunting. By the 19th Century they had been eliminated from most of North Africa; in southern Tunisia they were last seen in 1885; an entire herd of 20, one of the last in northern Algeria, was killed by a hunting party of French soldiers in the early 1920s. By that time they had been wiped out in all but the most inaccessible Saharan fastnesses: the great *ergs*, the Libyan *idehan*, the Ténéré and adjacent areas of northern Chad, and the Majabat. Here they were hunted by nomads in traditional ways.

Addax are slow and vulnerable and their survival depends on their ability to live in extreme desert conditions. They can be run down by dogs or exhausted by a hunter with a team of camels, since they cannot keep going for long on the hot sand. As long as they lived in places far from the wells that were essential to hunters, there was some hope for them. They were most persistently hunted by the Nemadi in the Majabat, but even the Nemadi could only stay in the waterless dunes for as long as their water-skins would support them. So they never killed enough addax to deplete their number permanently.

Nemadi hunters used the addax they did kill as a source of water for themselves. Addax do not store water in their stomach, but there is abundant digestive juice in the rumen. A hollow is made in the sand and

In the apparently empty dunes, many Saharan animals are given away by their tracks. Camels, gazelles and the stray hyena from the savannahs leave clear trails as they travel alone or in small parties. More confusing is the multiplicity of tiny tracks left round tufts of grass by jerboas, lizards, beetles and birds, all searching for food in the cool of morning or evening.

DORCAS GAZELLE HOOF MARKS

PAW MARKS OF HYENA

BEETLE TRACKS IN CLOSE-UP

LIZARD HOLE BY ARISTIDA GRASS

CAMEL TRAILS BETWEEN HAD BUSHES

CROSSROADS OF DESERT LARK AND JERBOA

lined with the skin of the dead animal. The horns are laid across the top to make a frame, the stomach is opened, and the vegetable matter inside is laid on the horns. In a short time an appreciable quantity of greenish liquid drips into the hollow below. In addition to its value to a hunter whose water has run out, the liquid is believed to have medicinal qualities: a family of addax hunters I once met in the desert north of Timbuktu assured me that this medicine would cure any illness.

Indeed addax medicine has an ancient history. The 14th-Century Berber traveller, Ibn Battuta, mentioned its wonderful properties, and at that time the liquid was exported to Tunis, together with the small calcareous lumps known as gazelle eggs, found occasionally in addax and gazelle stomachs. These lumps were used against scorpion bites, poison or witchcraft. Magical powers are also attributed to addax. The Tuareg of the Aïr mountains say that an addax, seeing a viper one day eating the grass which protected it from the bites of other vipers, immediately ate the grass too and became immune; from then on addax were able to attack vipers without danger, which is said to be why the Ténéré, where addax are widespread, is free of vipers. Some nomads carry talismen made of addax skin to protect them from harm.

Today these elite desert animals are relentlessly pursued by soldiers, oil prospectors and professional hunters armed with automatic weapons and four-wheel drive vehicles. The surviving addax are driven into ever more remote areas, and are now found chiefly in the Ténéré and northern Chad (where a special reserve has been set up for them), and in the Majabat in Mauritania, where the main population still lives. Here one observer found traces of over 5,000 addax in a single day in 1960, but later surveys show them to be in steep decline there also. It seems that the addax, a beautiful animal whose presence extends the boundaries of the habitable world into the heart of the world's harshest desert, is too exceptional an animal to be allowed to live, even in the deserted dunes for which it alone has been prepared by thousands of years of evolutionary hardship.

We searched for addax in the Admer Erg for three days, looking for their distinctive cow-sized footprints. On a hunch we visited places where they had not been recorded for many years. We found pastures of *had*, which would have been good addax country. Every day we saw parties of dorcas gazelle, which ran off in momentary alarm with their curious stiff-legged jumps, but always stopped after a few yards to watch us, apparently convinced we meant them no harm. But we found no traces of addax, and were forced to conclude that they had disappeared here as elsewhere. We could wait no longer, as our supplies were running out, and the camels needed water.

The camel's ability to do without water is generally much exaggerated. In fresh pasture after the rains, camels may spend a month or two without drinking, because they get enough water from the green plants. But for the rest of the year they must normally drink every few days. When most mammals including man, are short of moisture, they use up water from the blood plasma. If this continues too long, the blood becomes viscous and is unable to circulate properly or carry away heat, body temperature rises explosively, and the animal dies. The camel's hump stores fat, not water, but in case of need camels draw on water from their body tissues and thus avoid an explosive heat death.

On long trips away from the wells, camels lose up to a third of their body weight and replenish it afterwards by drinking up to 40 gallons of water at one go. As Théodore Monod points out, it is as if a person were to lose 50 pounds from thirst without harmful effects, and then drink 17 large bottles of mineral water to recover. By living on this water overdraft and by getting some liquid from plants, camels can make long journeys between wells. Monod once travelled 560 miles between Wadan in Mauritania and Arawan in Mali; on arrival at Arawan, his camels had not seen water for a month, but he had to force them to drink.

Our beasts were clearly not of this class, so we regretfully abandoned the search for addax, and turned back towards one of the wells on the edge of the *erg*. We reached it two days later, and spent a couple of hours drawing water. We took turns hauling the leaky leather bucket that seemed to lose half its load on the way up. The camels drank noisily from the bucket, trying to shoulder each other aside, and curling their upper lips in aristocratic disdain for the person who was working so hard for them. Near the well there were sandgrouse and desert sparrows, signs that we were out of the dune world where such profligate drinkers could not survive. When the camels had drunk their fill we set off again, back towards the date palms and irrigated gardens of Djanet.

Experts in Survival

To the untrained eye the desert is a barren place. Amid the few clumps of grass and thornbush, seared by the sun and whipped by wind and sand, little moves to relieve the lifeless monotony. But there is life and it survives only by means of special adaptations.

The chief problem of desert creatures is how to procure enough water to survive and then how to save it from being evaporated by the heat of the sun. Some species are small enough to escape underground or to seek the shade of rocks and vegetation where the desiccating powers of heat and wind are cut dramatically; others too large to hide are forced to tolerate the heat.

Insects, which get their liquids by feeding on either vegetation or other insects, are the most plentiful creatures of the Sahara. Along with other invertebrates like spiders and scorpions, they have an impermeable outer covering which prevents water loss by evaporation. This advantage, combined with their ability to hide away in the smallest refuges, contributes to their high rate of survival. Thus established, they form one of the first links of a food chain containing a variety of larger creatures.

Reptiles, including many lizards and snakes, as well as small mammals, notably the fennec fox and some rodents, derive from insects not just food but also a vitally important part of their liquids. These they retain by living underground or in the shade, emerging to hunt in the cool of morning, evening or night.

Birds also obtain much of their liquids from insects. But they need to drink regularly because they cool themselves by panting, which causes them to lose valuable water in their moisture-saturated breath. Small larks and finches stay close to rocky outcrops with trapped pools, or sip the dew from plants. Sandgrouse make long journeys to find water every day since they live in arid areas. The males carry water to the nestlings in their breast feathers.

The most common large mammals in the desert are gazelles. They take advantage of any shade afforded by rocks and trees and they conserve liquid by passing scarcely any water with the waste products in their urine. In some areas the dorcas gazelle can survive a long time without drinking since it gets most of its water from plants, while the addax, the white antelope of the desert, has evolved so that it rarely needs to drink at all.

A mantid nymph sits motionless on the desert floor, camouflaged among grains of sand that seem rock-sized beside it. It feeds exclusively on other insects, waiting patiently in ambush until they pass unsuspectingly within reach. Then it shoots out its forelegs and traps the prey in a vice-like grip.

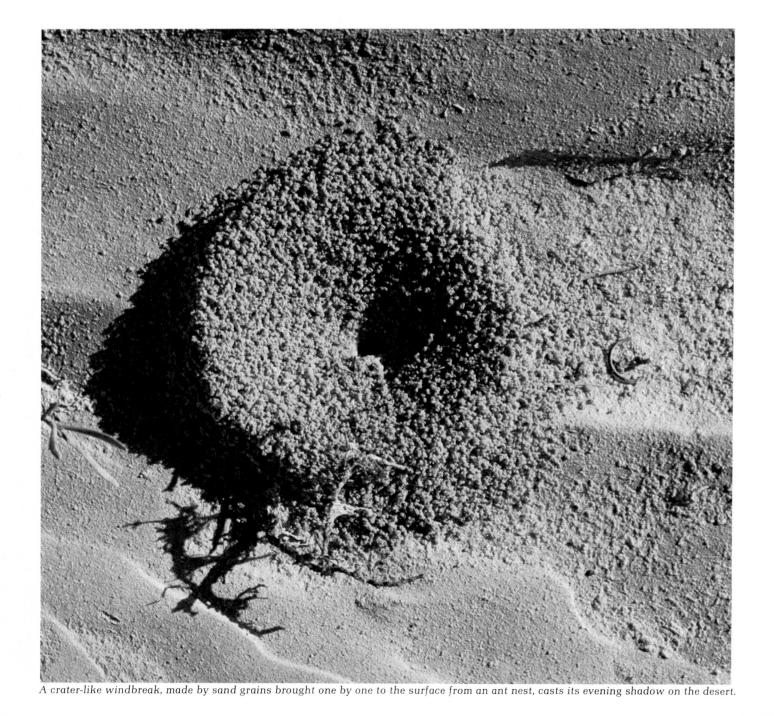

A crater-like windbreak, made by sand grains brought one by one to the surface from an ant nest, casts its evening shadow on the desert.

Inhabitants of an Underground City

Insects have ingenious ways of coping with desert conditions, apart from their impervious coverings, and the best example of sophisticated self-protection is provided by the ants. Ants are specialists in designing nests for different environments and in the Sahara they live in complex communities several feet beneath the surface.

Ants run the nest with an efficient division of labour. Some are entirely housebound. Bustling through the highways of the underground city, they collect grains of sand, carry them to the surface and deposit them around the entrance. They also keep the chambers tidy and wait on the swollen queen, whose life supply of eggs is stored in her body, or they look after newly emerged young.

Other worker ants brave the outside world to find food for the colony. They have several remarkable adaptations to ensure their safety as they scuttle across the hot sand. Many are covered in fine white hairs that are believed to reflect the heat. To guarantee a safe journey home, they have a built-in pedometer that registers how far they have travelled, and they take their bearings from the position of the sun.

When they find an important food source these indefatigable workers soon blaze an odour trail that can be easily followed by other workers, thus speeding up the food-gathering process and enabling reserves to be accumulated for times of hardship.

A tireless ant emerges from the darkness of its nest-hole with a grain of sand in its jaws.

A female wolf spider (above) picks her way delicately across barren ground, her abdomen covered with several layers of newly hatched spiderlings. In their first week, she carries them around for safety, taking them to shelter when necessary. If any fall off and fail to clamber back, they will be easy prey for other spiders and insects.

A beetle of the family Chrysomelidae (right), commonly known as a "bloody-nosed" beetle, rears up defensively, exuding the red, watery liquid after which it is named. Although this represents a water loss for the beetle it serves its purpose well, frightening many attacking birds that are used to the clear blood of most insects.

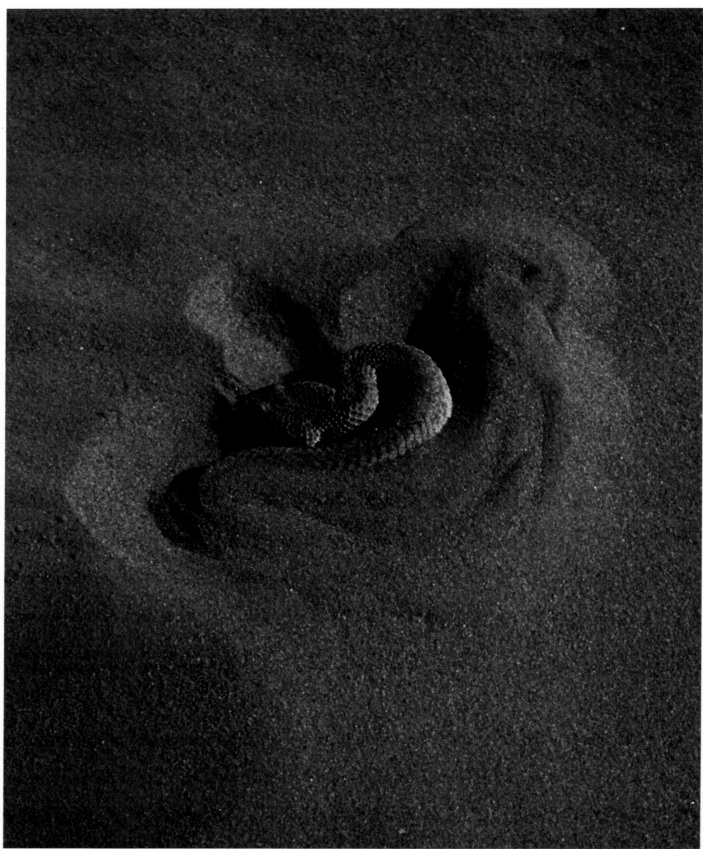

Wound up and ready to spring at its prey, a horned viper prepares for ambush by vibrating small projections on its body to work sand over it.

Creatures that Rely on Solar Energy

When reptiles such as lizards and snakes evolved from amphibians, they freed themselves from all ties with water. To combat the dehydrating powers of the sun they developed a thick, impervious skin and adapted their eggs by increasing the liquid around the embryo. But there was one important change they did not accomplish: they never acquired a constant blood temperature, and this evolutionary quirk dominates the reptiles' life in the Sahara today.

In the cold of night their temperatures fall so low that their bodies do not function efficiently. Their first requirement in the morning is to bask in the sun until their blood reaches its optimum temperature. Only then can they actively escape predators as they feed. But, if they stayed out too long, they would overheat, so they must often retire to the shade to let their blood cool.

As the sun rises high in the sky, the lizards disappear into their burrows. The spiny-tailed lizard (right) sometimes goes in head first and barricades the entrance of its refuge with its tough, protective tail.

A short, fat snake like the horned viper (left) cools down by burying itself in loose sand, where it lies in ambush for rodents and birds. At the vital moment it unleashes itself with a spray of sand. The poisonous fangs strike deeply, and if the prey retreats, the snake takes up the trail, sure to find its victim in its death throes nearby.

The short, slow legs of a spiny-tailed lizard condemn it to live close to its burrow.

Throat hackles extended, a lone raven sends its searching call echoing through the Tassili mountains. Perhaps a prospective mate will reply.

The Carefree Life of the Birds

Birds might seem at a disadvantage in the desert because they cannot burrow, but they have other ways of enduring the heat. They are protected by their insulating feathers and also by their high blood temperature which, by bringing them much closer to air temperature than other animals, cuts down their heat intake to a comparatively low level. They can expel this much heat by panting and, although they waste water in the process, they can fly to drinking places to replenish it.

One of the dramatic sights of the desert, when other creatures are hiding from the sun, is the raven (left), sentinel of the rugged outcrops. Its glossy plumage shines black and purple as it launches itself into the air, gliding through narrow corridors of rock to scour the cliffs for the corpses of fallen animals. The raven is safest in the sky, and when hunger forces it on to flat ground in search of small mammals, rodents and insects, it must remain constantly on the alert to the dangers of ground-dwelling predators, especially the jackal, which would not hesitate to drive it from any food it had found.

A bird that feels quite at home close to the ground is the mourning wheatear (right) which feeds exclusively on insects. Perched on the top of a rock or bush, it flips its tail and cocks its head, ever ready to dart out, twisting acrobatically in mid-air to seize a fly, or landing briefly on the hot ground to rummage for grubs.

Alighting on a sand-laden bush, a mourning wheatear waits expectantly for a meal.

A fennec, its sensitive ears alert, creeps stealthily forward in search of rodents and insects.

Living by a Strict Timetable

Small mammals like fennecs and jerboas can survive in the desert only if they avoid losing precious body liquid. The need to keep cool condemns them to follow a strict timetable, hunting for food when the sun is down and spending most of the day in different kinds of underground retreats.

The carnivorous fennec uses powerful limbs to tunnel as much as 30 feet into a dune, ending up about three feet below the surface of the sand. Here the temperature is agreeably cool and the world's smallest fox can sleep peacefully throughout the day, its huge ears conducting away excess heat.

The little plant-eating jerboa, weak in forelimb, cannot burrow far and has to seal off its short tunnel with a thin wall of sand to keep out the hot air. As it breathes in the confined space the jerboa creates a humid atmosphere. The air inhaled into the lungs absorbs unwanted body heat, and when exhaled condenses in the creature's cool nose to form moisture that can be absorbed.

Lying so close to the surface, the jerboa is vulnerable to marauding snakes. To prevent its life-saving refuge becoming its tomb, the jerboa builds an escape tunnel, also sealed against the heat. At the first signs of danger it explodes out of either exit, bounding off across the hot sand to find a safer place to hide before the sun saps its strength and leaves it to the mercy of predators.

A frightened jerboa springs high into the air on powerful hind legs, changing direction in a flurry of sand to throw off pursuit.

A small party of gazelles treks across an ocean of sand dunes in search of moisture-bearing vegetation. Occasionally the gazelles dig for water-storing roots, but normally they feed on plants or bushes above ground, selecting those which retain moisture, such as acacia, in preference to others that remain dry.

5/ Living Close to Nature

No man can live in the desert and emerge unchanged. He will carry, however faint, the imprint of the desert, the brand which marks the nomad. WILFRED THESIGER/ ARABIAN SANDS

At first it seems inexplicable that people can live in the Sahara: a desert the size of America, the only surface water a scattering of small pools. The very presence of people is so unlikely in this hostile place that there is an air of mystery about the nomads that does not wholly disappear even when they have become familiar. But by living among these people, one learns a great deal about the desert, its vegetation, wild-life, climate and the rhythm of life from day to day and year to year.

There are probably one and a half million nomadic herdsmen in the Sahara (in addition to half a million sedentary merchants and labourers in the oases). They live close to nature, moving families and tents so that their animals can feed on the new pasture that springs up after rain. Sometimes they hunt desert gazelle, and in times of famine they collect wild fruits or raid harvester ant stores for grass seeds.

Their lives are a collection of paradoxes. Living frugally and some-times dangerously, they have much leisure and are unhurried and re-laxed. They live on the edge of starvation but food is widely shared and nobody in need is abandoned. Cruel by reputation, they are in fact gentle, considerate and humorous. The Tuareg are among the fiercest and most warlike of the nomads (groups raided each other for camels until the 1930s), yet they have a rich oral literature, an alphabet of their own descended from ancient Phoenician, and treat their women with consideration, allowing them a liberty unique in the Muslim world.

Most of the peoples are pastoralists and fall into four main ethnic groups. Moors are found in the west, Arabs in the north, east and southeast. In the Tibesti mountains of northern Chad live the Teda, a dark-skinned people about whose origin little is known. The central Saharan mountains and southern fringes of the desert are dominated by the Tuareg, who are of Berber origin.

One group however—the Nemadi of Mauritania, generally regarded as Berbers—live by hunting alone. They despise people who live on camel and goat milk. "True Nemadi only eat meat," an old Nemadi hunter told me. Considered the lowest of the low by the Moor nomads, and "less than nothings", the Nemadi live in small groups at the wells along the edge of the Mréyyé, the remote sandy waste at the heart of the Mauritanian Empty Quarter. Some people think they may be vestiges of stone age hunters who once occupied the Sahara.

Nemadi normally hunt alone. A man leaves his family in the rudimentary shelter they inhabit, and goes off on foot with his dogs. He follows the tracks of a gazelle, and when he sights it, approaches stealthily under cover of the undulating dunes. The dog pack is released and soon runs the gazelle down. The pack leader, a carefully chosen and trained dog, reckoned to be more valuable than a camel, leaps for its ears or muzzle and holds on until the hunter kills the gazelle with his spear.

Several times a year the Nemadi join up for a long group hunt for addax or oryx which takes them deep into the heart of the wilderness of dunes that they alone enter. Several families come together and hire camels from the Moors against a promise of half a load of dried meat. (Most of the desert people have such trading links, since the desert itself cannot supply all the necessities of life.) Scouts go ahead, and the women follow with the camels, which are laden with water. As animals are killed, the meat is dried and loaded on the camels; bones are broken open for the marrow, and then buried so they shall not be profaned.

The Nemadi world is full of magic, and their hunting is deeply penetrated by small rites and observances. At night they sleep in the sand and trace the furrow of a snake alongside in the belief that it will keep real snakes away. In the evening, nobody talks of the next day's hunt in case the djenoun (spirits) overhear and warn the addax. Around the camp fire the hunters say, "I have no more bullets and I have lost my knife," in order to mislead the spirits. They take auguries of the forthcoming hunt: in the morning, if a hunting dog rolls in a tuft of grass it is a sign that blood will fall on his coat that day. The hunters have magic words which help or hinder their dogs, and during the hunt they refer to them as "pupils". The dogs are directed by gestures, and other signs enable the Nemadi to communicate among themselves silently in a secret language that the addax cannot hear, and the spirits above and the mother of the animals in the earth beneath do not understand. The dead addax is not named, but becomes "the one who let himself be taken", and as the hunter cuts up the meat he carefully avoids the wounds, "so as not to hurt him any more". In the evening they dance the dance of the animal they have killed.

In the rest of the open desert, the only inhabitants are the pastoral nomads of which the Tuareg are the best known and most spectacular. They are white Berbers, descended from the original inhabitants of northern Africa. The Arab invasions in the 7th and 11th Centuries submerged the Berber tribes in North Africa, but the Tuareg remained free and were able to defend the Sahara from Arab incursions. For centuries they controlled the rich trans-Saharan caravans that took slaves, gold and ivory to the Mediterranean. There are probably 3-400,000 Tuareg in the Sahara now, split into confederations that were independent until French colonial rule. Each of the main mountain ranges of the central Sahara—the Ahaggar, Tassili n Ajjer, Aïr and Adrar n Iforas—is inhabited by a separate Tuareg confederation, and others live in the dry Sahelian steppe along the southern edge of the desert, to the river Niger and beyond. The Tuareg are now divided politically between Algeria, Niger and Mali, with small numbers in Libya and Upper Volta, and their traditional herding and caravanning life is threatened by political and economic developments in the Sahara, and by the drought that has for several years affected the West African steppe.

I lived for several months in a Tuareg camp of the Kel Adrar confederation on the southern edge of the desert, studying the economy of these nomadic people. Life was unhurried and uneventful. I would wake shortly after first light, when a child brought a wooden bowl of goat's milk and left it beside my camp bed. Every morning the chief of the camp, Rhissa ag Amastane, sent me this customary present to a stranger, although he had lost many of his goats in the drought. From where our own tents were pitched I could see the people beginning to move in the scattered tents of Rhissa's camp about 50 yards away. Usually a child, dressed in black cloth, would be rounding up his father's goats and preparing to take them out for the day while his mother, dressed in a simple shift and shawl of the same cloth, rekindled the embers of last night's fire.

My Tuareg cook would already be up, making coffee on our fire. He was 18 and showed every sign of enjoying this trip, not so much for the wages

Tuareg camels carry salt from Bilma on a 350-mile trek to market in Agades. This ancient trade was threatened in the early 1970s by drought.

I was paying him, but for being at the centre of events in our camp which had become a meeting place for Tuareg from miles around. I had also lent him a sleeping bag and camp bed, which gave him prestige in the eyes of his friends. We slept in the open since there was no danger of rain or sandstorms at this time of year; it was early spring and the dry season was coming on.

The other person in our little group was my interpreter, Hamidine ag Illi, a Tuareg who had served for many years in the camel corps, and spoke good French. Known to everyone, he was my guarantor among the Tuareg; if he spoke for me, the nomads knew that I could be trusted not to be indiscreet with the answers they gave to my questions. Hamidine was aged about 40 and had been with me on my previous stay with these Tuareg. He clearly thought that a life of sitting on carpets asking questions about animals and pasture was a good one. He had quickly caught on to the subjects that interested me, and would often add questions of his own when he thought I had missed the point.

Many of my questions were directed at Rhissa who was over 70 years old, and had witnessed the declining power of the Tuareg from a fiercely independent race to a people weakened by famine and a changing world they no longer understood. With his help I was trying to build up a picture of how the Tuareg make a living in the desert.

Wherever the camp was made, the tents were pitched in approximately the same positions. Rhissa and his wife lived in the middle, in a small tent that was little more than a patchwork of blue and black cloth thrown over carved tent poles, vestiges of grander days when Rhissa had lived in a large leather tent with his children. They were all married now, and his sons with their families had their tents pitched around him. Rhissa's second son, Hami, with his wife and three children, had his tent 20 yards away, and Bai, the eldest son, was ten yards beyond that. Behind Bai were two tents pitched close together belonging to relatives of Rhissa's wife. One of the men was away looking for three of his camels that had been lost. On the other side, was the tent of Rhissa's youngest son Mohammed, and beyond him was that of Zayd and his wife. Zayd had no children, but he was supporting a 17-year old boy whose own family had been unable to look after him. In all there were 22 adults and 24 children but several of the men were away for most of the time I was there, on the long trips that are characteristic of nomads: one to sell sheep, another to search for work in Algeria.

Life in the nomad camps does not change much from day to day, but each has its own rhythm. I remember one spring day in particular. When

A Tuareg nomad peers through the slit in his veil—a cloth some five yards long, traditionally wound around the head. In a reversal of the usual Muslim practice, Tuareg men—but not women—are veiled from puberty onwards. The practical purpose of the veil is to offer protection from sun and blowing sand to the herdsmen during their long periods in the desert. But this has become ritualized so that even in camp the veil is rarely removed.

I awoke, Zayd was getting together the few milking camels and their young that had spent the night at the camp. The riding camels and females that had not given birth this year were away at pasture in the care of a teenage boy, and rarely came here. Most of Zayd's camels had died in the drought, and he looked after other peoples' animals in return for a share of the milk. The camels had started to browse on the thorn trees of the wadi, but Zayd moved them slowly away from the camp, the older females grunting unhappily.

I laid out a carpet under a thorn tree, where there would be shade later in the day when the sun was high, and talked to Hamidine about the day's programme. Today I had invited Rhissa to my tent for talks, and now we were awake he walked over. He was about six foot two, tall even for a Tuareg, and wore a faded black cotton robe, with baggy trousers of the same stuff, held up by a decorated leather draw-string. He had leather sandals, decorated with a red and yellow design, and carried a heavy stick which hung from his wrist by a looped cord. Round his neck there were several flat red leather pouches containing verses from the Koran as a protection against illness and evil spirits, and another was tied round his right arm just above the elbow. He also wore a silver ring with a triangular stone set in it. Despite his age and a slow, apparently painful walk, he was slim and upright and his lined, hawkish face was calm—an impressive man in any context.

The most striking part of Tuareg dress is the veil worn by all adult men. Rhissa's veil was made of the same black cloth as the rest of his clothes, and consisted of a strip five yards long wound several times round his face and head, so that only his eyes showed. Some Tuareg are still formal about their veils, and hitch them up to the bridge of their noses when meeting strangers, but over the weeks I had been talking to Rhissa he had relaxed occasionally, to the point of not bothering to pull his veil right up again when it slipped. He also no longer bothered when I was with him to drink tea underneath his veil in the formal manner, but pulled the veil down and drank directly.

Rhissa was accompanied by one of his sons, identically dressed but with a long sword in a red leather scabbard slung at his waist. When they were ten yards away, Rhissa dropped his stick to the ground and called out the formal greeting "*salaam aleykum*", waiting for our response "*aleykum salaam*" before approaching. I stepped forward and shook his hand in the manner of the Tuareg, letting the palm of my hand touch his, drawing it slowly back so that my fingers ran across his palm, and then pulling my hand back to touch my chest. Rhissa sat on my small rectangular carpet, and the others arranged themselves as best they could around us. There were too many people to form a circle, and somebody ended up with his back to the rest of us.

I had noticed that Mohammed had moved his tent 100 yards away beyond the camp. I asked Rhissa why and he said that Mohammed's wife had quarrelled with one of the other women, but he would not tell me the reason for the row. Such a move seemed to be an accepted part of camp life, and in this case Mohammed had not left the camp but had simply moved away from the immediate cause of friction. Camps sometimes split for such reasons; the ability to move makes nomad life remarkably free of the nagging quarrels that can divide small villages.

I asked Rhissa if he remembered the camel raids that used to take place between Tuareg and other nomads in this part of the desert.

"Of course I do," he replied. "They continued until I was a young man and married for the first time. The Reguibat of Mauritania used to come every year, and they killed my father. Other men chased the Reguibat and killed them, and got back the camels they had taken."

As we talked, the other men listened attentively, absorbed by the story of events they had heard often before. Rhissa was sure of his memory, recalling names and places with ease. He identified years by notable events: "that was the year many children died of measles; that year there was good pasture in the north and the wadis flowed for several days." The others were silent out of respect for the old man, but when I spoke they laughed gently at my mispronunciation of Tuareg names, and at my questions which revealed such ignorance of nomad life. But it was clear that they enjoyed talking about these things, and found nothing unusual in the fact that an outsider shared their interest. "Why do you ask these questions?" Rhissa had said to me a few days after I had set up camp near him, and the men seemed satisfied when I answered that people in my country had heard of the Tuareg and wanted to know how they made a living in the desert. When he had an important point to make, Rhissa leant forward and touched me lightly on the arm. When I pressed him on an apparent inconsistency in his story, Rhissa showed a flash of irritation. "Why do you ask me all these questions? I am old and cannot remember. Ask one of the young men." But in a moment he was calm again.

After two hours of talk, Rhissa was tired, and I walked back to his tent with him as there were things I wanted to see in the camp. Several of the tents, like Rhissa's, were made of a patchwork of sky blue and black cloth. Two were made, more traditionally, of goat skins, tanned and dyed with dark red clay, and sewn together. It used to be possible to judge a person's status by the number of skins in his tent, an important chief having 60 or 70, while 30 or 40 were used for a more modest tent.

The tents in Rhissa's camp were spread over square wooden frames made of bars across four upright poles, which were carved into simple decorated shapes, emphasized by cross-hatchings burned into the wood. The edges of the tent were pegged down at the northern and southern ends, but were left open on the side facing away from the sun. Several of the tents had grass matting wind shields, decorated with geometric patterns picked out in coloured leather thongs. These wind shields were up to ten yards long, and were kept wound and upright against the tent poles, so that they could be unrolled easily when the wind began to blow.

The sand around the tents was brushed clean each morning, and a carpet was put down if visitors came. Hami's tent had a typical collection of nomad belongings. At one end was his camel saddle, and his sword hung from the tent pole above it, next to a leather bag in which Hami put all his belongings when camp was moved. A wooden bowl for milk stood in one corner, in a stand to keep it beyond the reach of children and small animals. A wooden funnel hung on the tent pole; it was used for pouring milk into a small skin bag to make butter and cheese. In the same corner there was a brass tea tray, a leather box with six tea glasses and a blue enamel tea pot.

At the other end of the tent, Hami's wife had her belongings. A leather bag for her effects was decorated in pale green, red and yellow, and was strung with strips of leather and tassels of the same colours. The bag was closed with a square brass padlock, of the simple type made by Tuareg smiths. The key was about nine inches long and also made of brass, and Hami's wife wore it tied to the end of her shawl; it was thrown over her shoulder and hung down her back to hold the shawl in place. At her end of the tent there were also two leather cushions and some cooking pots. Hanging on a thorn tree outside was a goat-skin *guerba* dripping slowly, keeping its remaining water cool by evaporation.

Hami's wife was outside the tent, and although she would not sit with us on the carpet, she listened to the conversation. She was dressed like the other women of the camp in black cloth; her hair was parted in the middle and tightly plaited into several braids that hung down to her shoulders on either side. She wore a coloured bead necklace and a white pendant made from diamond-shaped white stones, and three red leather bracelets with chequer patterns of coloured beads. A leather tobacco pouch hung round her neck, and from time to time she took some strands of tobacco from it to chew.

Hami's wife was working a piece of leather as she listened to us. Tuareg women make the things every family needs, such as bags and cords, and although there are few art objects in Tuareg life, most utilitarian things are decorated with geometric designs in brightly coloured leather. Beside her there was also a *guerba* in preparation. The goatskin had been folded back and removed without being cut except at the neck and feet. It had been tanned with an extract of tree bark and left to dry in the sun. Later each foot would be tied with cord made from desert grasses and the neck would be given a cord with which the *guerba* could be closed when it was full. In this way the goatskin made a very manageable container for 20 or 30 litres of water.

Keeping the camp supplied with water is one of the main chores of nomad life. It is rare for the Tuareg to camp close to a well, since the peace is constantly broken by animals on their way to water. So they set up their tents several miles from a well, and every day somebody has to take the empty *guerbas* and a donkey to fetch drinking water for the family. This job is normally given to the children, and Hami's three children were preparing to set off with a donkey and two empty *guerbas*. The oldest, an eight-year old boy, had a herdsman's stick like his father and was taking his task seriously, marshalling the two smaller girls to look after the donkey while he went ahead.

All three children were dressed identically, in a strip of black cloth with a hole in the centre through which they put their heads so that the cloth hung down loosely in front and behind without being sewn up at the sides. The boy's head was shaved except for a crest of hair running from his forehead back across the middle of his skull, and the girls had this same crest and a small tuft of hair on either side.

Hami was preparing the first of the day's rounds of tea with typically elaborate ceremony. He laid out three or four dead thorn branches with their ends together, and lit some kindling of dried grass beneath them. The dry branches flared quickly, and when they had burned a little, Hami made a small hollow in the sand beside the fire, and swept some of the glowing cinders into it. Then he filled a battered kettle from the *guerba* and put it on the cinders. He had beside him the glasses and a teapot on a brass tray, and with one of the glasses he measured tea leaves from a bag, dumping them into the pot, adding boiling water from the kettle, and putting the pot on the fire to brew. He then took a conical sugarloaf from the bag, and, using the base of a glass, knocked off a piece of sugarloaf and added it to the pot.

With spare, precise gestures Hami arranged the glasses in a line close together on the tray, and poured tea into each of them. He lifted the pot so that the tea fell a foot or more in a pale brown arc, and splashed into a head of froth in each glass. He returned the tea to the pot from each glass, and poured it out again with the same gestures. He repeated this several times, and finally poured a little into a glass to taste. Satisfied that the tea was sufficiently sugared and aerated, he poured a glass for each of the men present, and we drank the scalding brew with loud sucking noises in the approved fashion. As we did so, Hami filled the pot again with water from the kettle and put it back on the embers.

The same sequence of gestures was repeated twice more, and each time more sugar was forced into the pot so that the brew became a strong sugary syrup. In the last round, Hami pushed green mint leaves into the pot. The precision with which he arranged the glasses on the tray suggested a ritual act of ancient standing in Tuareg society. But although nomad life now seems inconceivable without it, tea is in fact a recent luxury, having spread across the Sahara from Morocco only around the end of the last century.

Hamidine and I returned to our camp for a lunch of rice and mutton. The sun was at its hottest now, an indistinct fierce white circle directly overhead. One of the men had draped a striped Tuareg blanket in the branches of a thorn tree to throw a little shade on the ground where the carpet was laid. The heat made every movement an effort as though the hot air had gained weight and was pressing in on arms and legs. While we waited for the afternoon cool, Hamidine taught me a Tuareg game.

With his fingers he made a chequer board of small holes in the sand, eight down and six across. Each of us had a pile of counters. Mine were whitish pebbles and Hamidine had black pellets of camel dung, and with these we filled the board, leaving one empty place. The game was to move one counter in turn, trying always to get three of your own in a straight line, while preventing your opponent from doing likewise. Each time you did this, you removed one of the opposing pieces. Hamidine beat me three times, before deciding that I was no match for him. For a while we played *isseren*, tossing six split sticks into the air and scoring points according to how many fell with the split side uppermost, but the effort of collecting and throwing the sticks was too much in the heat. So I was content to sit with my back resting against the thorn tree and read.

A Tuareg herdsman who has watered his stock of goats and camels at a well prepares to return them to the sparse desert pastures.

Around three-thirty, Hami brought three riding camels to our camp for an afternoon trip to the well. Chewing meditatively, the animals crouched in the insufficient shade of an acacia tree and waited. Mounting a camel was always a nervous moment for me. While the animal crouched, I climbed into the saddle and, with a tug of the rein and a cry, urged it to its feet. It straightened its hind legs with a jolt that threw me forward and threatened to impale me on the spiked pommel of the saddle and then did the same with its front legs, throwing me hard against the back of the saddle. Comfortably seated with my bare feet on the camel's neck, I urged the beast forward by pushing rhythmically with my legs and steering with the single rein.

We rode off in single file. The easy swaying motion of the camel was hypnotic and restful. I could see the low rolling sand plains stretching away to the east beyond the line of the wadi we were following. A dusty haze hung in the air, but the aggressive midday heat had gone. As the camels walked along we passed a family moving camp, their baggage loaded on to a camel and a donkey. Two long curved tent poles were slung on one side of the donkey, balanced on the other side by a rolled up windscreen mat. Several yellow and green blankets were thrown across the donkey's back, making a comfortable seat. A woman sat on this perch, a newly born lamb peering nervously from the folds of her robe.

The well was three miles down the wadi, a small hole in the ground surrounded by people and animals. Flocks of goats and groups of camels were arriving across the wadi bed, patiently waiting their turn, standing or sitting close together. The camels wandered off from time to time to browse on an acacia tree or to nose their way to the water, but they were firmly kept in place by their herdsmen with a rap on the nose. A boy was drawing water; he stood with his feet firmly planted on either side of the opening and hauled up a leather bucket, emptying it into an enamel bowl at his feet, where his goats pushed one another aside to get at the water. When the goats had drunk their fill, a child led them a few yards away to the shade, and the camels were watered—a slower process, since they emptied the bowl as fast as the boy could fill it. Eventually they were satisfied and wandered off, and another herdsman took the boy's place at the well.

The well was obviously an important social centre. While the smaller children played together among the animals, the older girls and boys gossiped and flirted. Several people were washing clothes and veils, hanging them to dry on nearby thorn bushes. Four children arrived with donkeys and empty *guerbas*; when their turn came, they laid the goatskins on the ground beside the well and filled them carefully, one child holding the neck of the *guerba* open as the oldest boy poured in water from the leather bucket. The full *guerbas* were then slung beneath the donkey's belly by cords across its back, with a pad of old cloth to stop the cords rubbing. Meanwhile, two small boys were making grass cord snares to catch sandgrouse that would come to the well to drink in the evening after the people and animals had gone.

Each person had brought his own leather well-bucket and cord of tree-bark fibre, and we borrowed one of these to fill our own *guerbas*. When the job was done I walked a few yards to where a man was digging a new well. Using a simple iron pick, he had dug ten feet down into the wadi bed, and already water was trickling into the bottom of his hole. He would dig a few feet more and then line the opening at the top with acacia branches to strengthen it. These shallow wells in wadi beds are easy but not dependable sources of water, liable to dry up in summer. More substantial wells go down to the main ground-water table. Some reach very great depths: the record in the southern Sahara is probably held by a well in the Azawad in Mali which is over 300 feet deep. Wells of this size can hardly have been dug all at one time, but have presumably been deepened progressively over the centuries as water was used up. At these depths special leather cords are needed, and the full bucket is pulled up by a camel hitched to a pulley. Tuareg measure the depth of wells by the number of men who can stand in them upright with their arms stretched above their heads, and for a moment I wondered idly how many upright men would fit in the Azawad well.

Leaving the well, we mounted our camels again and rode out towards the dunes. I wanted to see Rhissa's herd of camels which were at pasture several miles away in the care of one of his sons. They went to drink at the well every third or fourth day, but otherwise stayed where the pasture was good. We rode at a fast swaying trot across low undulating sand waves. After about an hour some camels came into sight, recognizable as Rhissa's by the brands on their necks. The boy who was looking after them stood up as we approached. He was on his own out here for several days at a time, only meeting people when he took the camels to the well, and seemed pleased to see us.

We dismounted, pushing the camels down by pressing with our feet on the animals' necks, hobbled them without unsaddling, and sat under a tree. Hamidine gathered dry twigs and made a fire, and the herd boy started brewing the tea and sugar we had brought with us. The boy talked about his animals: how one of them seemed ill, and another had been frightened in the night, perhaps by a jackal, and had fled several miles, and how he had tracked it the following morning and brought it back. He thought that the pasture at this place was nearly exhausted, and asked us to tell Rhissa that he would like to take the animals a few miles farther south where one of the boys at the well had told him there was good greenery. We in turn told him the news from the camp: that Bai had gone south to sell his sheep, and that Zayd had found a white riding camel that had been lost.

Then we walked over to the camels which were browsing on the top branches of some acacias. I started to ask about them. The boy remembered clearly all the details of each animal's life. "This one is five years old, and was given to Rhissa by his brother; she has not yet had a calf. This one was born in Rhissa's herd 12 years ago; she had a calf in her fourth year, but it was eaten by jackals; two years later she had another calf, and that is the animal you see over there. Two years later she had a male calf; Rhissa exchanged it for some grain a few weeks ago with a trader from the south." The camels continued their noisy chewing, occasionally curling their upper lips to display yellow-stained teeth.

While we talked about the camels, a young man appeared over the dunes. He was carrying two spring traps made from branches bound together with grass cord. He told us that many of his goats had died and that he was off to hunt gazelle. I asked him whether there were not easier ways than the cumbersome spring traps.

"If I had some camels it would be easy to chase the gazelle until they were exhausted, and then kill them with a spear, but I have none. So I must hunt like this." When I asked how his family managed for food while he was away, he replied that his wife had been gathering wild grass seeds by raiding harvester ant granaries, and that she had enough for the moment. He hurried off when we had finished talking, eager to set his traps before nightfall. Hamidine and I remounted our camels, and turned back towards our camp.

When we arrived, it was almost dark. The air was fresh and cool, and a fire was crackling next to my carpet. The animals had been brought in for the night, and Zayd was milking the camels. At the other tents, goats were being milked, and the young goats were attached to the kid rope for the night. A *marabout*, or holy man, had come to visit me and was waiting; I wrapped myself in a burnous against the mounting cold and we settled down on my carpet to talk. After a while Zayd joined us with a wooden bowl of camel milk. I drank a little and handed it on.

The *marabouts* have several functions among the Tuareg in addition to their religious role: they administer traditional justice, settle quarrels and practise a kind of quack medicine. They are the learned men, for whom the Koran has an answer to every problem, but since few other Tuareg can read Arabic, the *marabouts* tend to invent Koranic stories on the spur of the moment to justify a particular course of action. They are paid for their services in animals, and try to exact tithes as well; as a consequence many are quite rich.

This man was clearly worried that I might threaten his position, both by my knowledge of the outside world, and by my medicine chest, which was in constant demand among the nomads. The day before I had disinfected and bandaged the burned arm of a little girl who had fallen in a camp fire. Before doing this I had to wash off an encrusted pack of mud and camel dung put there on the instructions of this *marabout*. He had obviously come to complain, and to reassert his authority.

We talked for a while about the history of the Tuareg, on which I had been questioning the *marabouts*, but his information was vague and contradictory. The other men around the carpet listened intently. Coming from a world of books and newspapers, radio and television, I found it difficult at first to realize how different life is without sure and diverse sources of information. Among the desert Tuareg nothing is certain; all is rumour, opinion and fifth-hand gossip. Commonplace and wild surmise are inextricably mixed in most nomads' minds. The *marabouts* are respected for their learning, but people know that much of what they say is untrue. One of the recurring themes of conversation of Tuareg camps is the desire to distinguish between truth and false-hood, and as an outsider I was thought to be a useful judge in these matters. I was often consulted in a roundabout way, and this evening's discussion with the *marabout* quickly turned into such a session.

"Some people here say that men have walked on the moon," Hamidine said tentatively, looking at the white disc that had appeared above the horizon. When I said it was indeed so, they all nodded wisely, as though they had known it all along, muttering about the cleverness of the *Kel Ehendeset*—"the people who make and manipulate machines", a term used to describe a technological conglomerate nation made up indiscriminately of Europe, America and the Soviet Union and which figures largely in Tuareg notions about the world beyond the desert. "No," said the *marabout*, "God would never allow men to visit the moon. He merely put them in a tent and made them think they had been there, so they would tell everyone when they came back. It is clearly impossible for men to go to the moon. God would never allow it." The seated Tuareg looked confused again.

Hamidine leant over to me and said quietly that although he was not sure about the moon, he knew that it was the rain that made the trees grow, but that he had had an argument with this same *marabout* who maintained that God alone made the trees grow. I asked the *marabout* about the rain and he replied that each raindrop was a vehicle for *angeloussen*, God's messengers who carried out his orders. The *angeloussen* were responsible for making all the *Kel Ehendeset*'s machines work—there were *angeloussen* making aeroplanes fly and lorries move. Many *angeloussen* could travel in a single raindrop, and in a moment of cultural atavism I asked how many could fit on the head of a pin. This started a heated scholastic argument between the men.

The *marabout* put an end to this by telling a story about America. It was told in the Koran, he said, that in America each day lasted a whole year. This gave rise to a difficult problem for the Muslim faithful in that country: should they each day say a day's prayers, or a whole year's? He asked the assembled men for their opinion, and when none was able to reply, triumphantly announced that the answer, also written in the Koran, was that in America a year's prayers should be said each day. His pleasure in this piece of learning was in no way diminished when I pointed out that the existence of America was not even suspected when the holy book was written. The Tuareg looked from me to him, unable to make up their minds about our relative probity. I was a genuine *Kel Ehendeset*, but they had to live with him when I had gone, and I fancied that they would probably finish by half believing both of us as insurance against the uncertain world outside.

Our food was brought, a thick millet porridge that was a welcome change from the rice and mutton we had been eating exclusively for the last ten days. We all ate silently, the Tuareg men sitting cross-legged or reclining on one elbow, their veiled faces lit indistinctly by the flickering light of the fire. As we finished, people began to drift over from Rhissa's camp and other neighbouring groups, as I had let it be known that I would have tea and chewing tobacco for anyone who came and sang or played the traditional Tuareg musical instruments.

Some children gathered first, and I started a competition for the best animal fable. These stories, which have the unmistakeable stamp of animal fables from the world over, are a source of great amusement to the children, who spend hours telling them. The winner that evening,

A young camel which has collapsed and died of thirst decomposes in the desert. In its frantic efforts to find its feet, it scoured a shallow grave in the form of a camel hoof print. The carcass has already become food for other creatures including a raven whose tracks can be seen entering the hollow (bottom right).

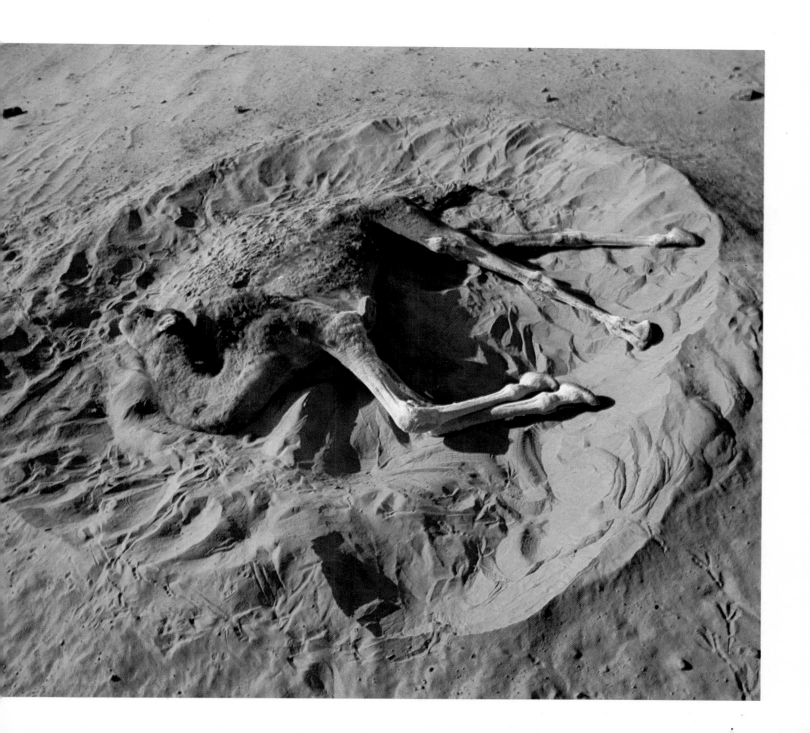

one of Rhissa's grandchildren, was rewarded with a large lump of sugar. His story was about the jackal and its hereditary enemy, the hyena. "Jackal had been teasing Hyena too much," the boy said, "and for revenge, Hyena hid in Jackal's hole when he was out, in order to ambush him. When Jackal returned he stopped a hundred yards from his hole and shouted, 'Hole, how are you?' After a moment's silence he repeated, louder this time, 'Hole, why don't you reply this evening?' Hyena thought further silence would make Jackal suspicious, and so he made a noise. Warned by this, Jackal ran away."

By the time the children had finished their stories of animal cunning and perfidy, men and women had gathered. The women who by day hid their faces by turning away or drawing across a shawl, were more at ease now around the fire in the semi-darkness. They talked in confident voices, calling out to newcomers, and laughing at the children's stories. One woman from a neighbouring camp was renowned for her skill with the *imzad*, the single-string violin. She had put together an *imzad* this evening by stretching a skin across an enamel bowl, adding a wooden arm and a taut string which was probably a goat's tendon. She tuned this for a few moments, and then began to sing in a loud nasal tone. The other women and the men joined in a chorus from time to time.

The singing was spirited, with variations around a single note that were monotonous to my unpractised ear at first, but that soon became a lulling chant. I could follow no more than a few words of the song, which recounted the adventures of a man who left on a dangerous and distant trip. Occasionally the men and women whispered to one another, and there was some laughing and giggling among a group of teenage boys and girls in the darkness beyond the flickering light of the fire.

Late that evening, after the tea had gone round several times, the Tuareg drifted away and I was left in silence with my Tuareg cook and Hamidine. The stars shone with that peculiar brilliance they have in the clear desert air, and Orion was swinging slowly across the silent sky. I could hear indistinct sounds from Rhissa's camp, children laughing still despite the hour, and men talking. A young camel in the distance roared morosely for its mother, and nearer there was the chomping and ruminating of camels feeding on the thorn trees. A dog ran silently hither and thither around the camp, looking for scraps of food.

I asked Hamidine what he would do if he became very rich overnight, and he answered after a moment that he would buy five lorries and fill them with grain; every evening he would have a party like ours for the nomads who did not have food; they would eat, a pretty girl would play the *imzad*, and they would sing together. It was a pleasant thought.

A year later in the Tassili mountains in the eastern Sahara, a thousand miles from Rhissa's camp, I was walking with a donkey train of baggage along the old caravan route that runs from Djanet to Ghat. A young Tuareg man carrying a small leather bag of possessions overtook our cumbersome caravan, walking fast in the same direction. As he passed I greeted him, and he turned and looked at me through the slit of his raised veil; after a moment's hesitation he strode over and clasped me warmly with both arms. It was Hami ag Rhissa, with whom I had spent so much time the year before.

We halted at once and made tea under the shade of an overhanging rock. After asking about my family, and my travels since I had left his father's camp, he told me his news. Rhissa and his wife were dead. Bai, the eldest son, was now chief of the camp. Most of the camels and goats had died in the drought and the nomads were living on their remaining handfuls of grain, and on help that cousins and friends had given them. The rains had failed again, and there was no pasture. I asked about the children. Two of his own children and several of the other children in the camp had died of measles that winter.

We finished the third glass of tea, and he stood up. He had to go, he said. He was on his way to Libya, where he had heard there was work in the oilfields. If God was kind to him he would work for a few months and make enough money to return home and buy new animals. Then he could start the proper life of the desert again, and feed his family. He would ask God to help me in my journey, and take me home safely. With these words he set off again down the narrow track eastwards, and disappeared behind the twisted rock pillars of the ravine.

The Cooling Sky

Usually empty and monotonously pale blue during the day, the Saharan sky sometimes changes radically between late afternoon and early morning. As the sun sets, clouds may gather above the horizon and then vanish, giving way to the moon and stars. Dawn may bring new, thicker clouds, gently lit from behind.

Typically the sky is clear of clouds until the end of the day when the currents of warm air thrown off by the hot desert surface have risen sufficiently to cool and condense any water vapour present. Such clouds, usually cauliflower-shaped cumulus about a mile up, are too thin and too easily dispersed to provide rain. The minute droplets of which they consist must grow a million times by colliding with other droplets in order to fall as rain. Before this happens the clouds usually vanish: as the sun sets, the temperature of ground and air balance out and the sky clears once more.

For the traveller disoriented by the desert's daytime void, darkness reduces the Sahara to more manageable proportions. He finds in the stars constant and predictable points of reference. Each night, according to the season, the constellation of the Swan flies majestically along the line of the Milky Way or the Scorpion rises lethargically over the horizon, turning slowly on its side as the night advances. On waking, the traveller can tell by the position of Vega or some other star whether to sleep again or wait for camp to stir.

The night sky is also a point of reference for the nomads. The position of the "Female Camel"—the Great Bear—directs them to the Pole Star, by which they navigate on night marches. The rising of Orion and the Pleiades warn of summer storms. But, used to mirages in the day, nomads accept in their folklore the possibility of illusion at night. According to one legend, the stars are no more than tiny holes in the tent the Gazelle threw over the earth in an attempt to entrap her lover, the Bustard, who always left her before dawn to avoid revealing his ugliness.

Dawn sometimes brings dramatic cloud patterns again, usually over the mountains. During the night, the rock becomes cold and gradually cools the air above it. Cumulus clouds form two miles up and thin layers of cirrus four miles up. But these clouds too are ephemeral. The heat of the sun soon evaporates them and the sky takes on once more its pale daytime hue.

SUNSET OVER MOUNTAINS NEAR THE OASIS OF SILET

LATE EVENING CUMULUS OVER THE AHAGGAR

A FULL MOON REPLACES THE SETTING SUN AT SILET

FIRST LIGHT OF DAWN IN THE TASSILI MOUNTAINS

CUMULUS FILLING THE EARLY MORNING SKY

AÏR ROCK AGAINST CUMULUS AND CIRRUS

CIRRUS HERALDING SUNRISE

EARLY MORNING IN THE FOOTHILLS OF THE AHAGGAR

6/ The Silent Plains

The desert is the Garden of Allah, from which the Lord of the Faithful removed all superfluous human and animal life, so that there might be one place where he can walk in peace.

ARAB SAYING

West of the Ahaggar mountains, the land changes with startling abruptness. The granite foothills lose their coherence, become scattered sugar-loaves in an empty plain, then disappear altogether. The lava is replaced by a firm floor of black gravel. This is the start of the gravel plains or *reg* of the Tanezrouft, which stretch westward towards Mauritania, and south to the savannahs of tropical Africa 500 miles away.

The *reg* are the quintessential Saharan landscape. They cover the largest areas in the desert and are among the most hostile places on earth, almost devoid of life; by comparison, the rest·of the Sahara seems rich in plants and animals. The Tanezrouft is a typical *reg*— four times the size of England and a major hazard for the Tuareg nomads who cross it in a series of forced marches with the sheep they take from the Adrar n Iforas to the markets in Algeria. There are only half a dozen wells and to miss one or find it dry is probably to die.

I had come to the Tanezrouft because it seemed a good place to see the Sahara at its most extreme and to investigate my own reactions to the wilderness. I began my journey at the tiny oasis of Silet at the westernmost edge of the Ahaggar chain. The map, inaccurate for most of the Sahara, here becomes downright misleading. Map makers hate a void, and fill up empty spaces with names of wadis that have been dry for several thousand years, with frontiers and with useful instructions for people who wish to use the trans-Saharan track that runs down the western side of the Tanezrouft a few hundred miles away. A single well, with its conventional symbol and name written large, covers a quantity of empty space and seems impossible to miss. Silet, drawn in with a tiny palm tree, looks imposing.

In reality, it is different. Sufficient water just below the surface has enabled a few Tuareg to irrigate some patches of garden. There are tents next to primitive houses made of mud brick, as if the Tuareg were caught in an uneasy compromise between the nomadic and the settled life.

At Silet I was to pick up a Tuareg guide named Atitel who knew the Tanezrouft, having once been a caravanner travelling to the south. We were to spend several days in the Tanezrouft, driving out to a remote well in the centre of the reg, at a place called Timmissao, where there were said to be low cliffs and some vegetation. I had heard about Timmissao from Tuareg who occasionally stopped there on their caravans, and it sounded mysterious and appealing, a place on a human scale in the middle of the flat emptiness of the Tanezrouft.

On a camel, this would have taken a week or two, but in a Land Rover the reg are easily accessible, because the hard gravel is an excellent surface for driving. With a good guide, maps and the necessary navigational aids—like the two compasses I had with me—it is possible to explore the reg with comparatively little danger. The purist will complain that doing things in the deserts by vehicle takes away most of the romance. All the great journeys were made by camel, and there is no doubt that this added much mystique, as well as hardship. There are still many areas that can only be visited by camel. But many of the rewards of wilderness travel are no less in a vehicle, and the challenge is still there. If you break down in the Tanezrouft you may have to walk 200 miles to find water and search for a well-head consisting of no more than a hole in the ground. In any case, the merits of camel versus car are quite relative. As Ralph Bagnold, who did his exploration in a Ford, pointed out, Roman travellers must have felt the same sense of sacrilege when the hideous camel was introduced to the Sahara, destroying all the romance of donkey journeys.

I found Atitel in his tent next to a small garden, and he agreed at once to go with me. He put a blanket, some food, his teapot and glass into an old army kitbag, and was ready to leave. We took wood for our camp fires and filled our jerrycans, and the two guerbas that hung on the outside of the Land Rover, at his well. From the well, narrow irrigation channels fed a small garden where water-melons and onions were growing. A makeshift hedge of thick green bushes kept the goats at bay, and in it was a willow warbler, an emigrant from Europe on its way south to winter in tropical Africa. A small flight of wading birds turned and banked over another irrigated garden a few hundred yards away.

We climbed into the Land Rover and set off towards the south-west. A donkey track led along a wadi bed with a few dusty thorn trees, and then up towards a low pass through granite rocks that marked the end of the Ahaggar chain. At the top I stopped to work out our position and course. There was a spectacular view, with the mountains where I had spent the last few weeks behind us, and the Tanezrouft in front. Here the granite rocks of the Ahaggar disappeared into the gravel-covered surface of the ancient Saharan shield. The grey boulders were piled loosely on top of each other. Their shapes had been eroded for centuries so that some were finely balanced on one or two points and seemed to sway slightly in the wind. The hard white sand floor of the pass was made of quartz grains shading imperceptibly into the gravel of the plain.

We drove down into the reg and headed towards a low hill just visible on the horizon. The plain seemed entirely level, with a surface of greyish-black pebbles, and for the first hour or two Atitel was confident of his route, since there were landmarks to steer by: here and there black conical mounds a hundred feet high rose from the gravel and a straggling line of acacias followed an underground trace of moisture. Because of the nearness of the mountains, some water must have drained off into the reg, following a wadi so shallow it was invisible. On either side there were tide marks made by a sudden torrent the last time it had rained, probably several years ago. To the north the hills had jagged outlines, but except for the black mounds the other horizons were all disconcertingly horizontal. The only sign of life was a digger wasp, and two flies that were probably following the vehicle.

It was almost midday, and very hot. There were mirages in every direction, so that acacia trees and small hills seemed to float uneasily above the ground. A heat haze blurred the top of the mirages, troubling the reflections with ripples. The sky was pale blue, flecked with wispy white clouds and fading at the horizon into the greyish pebbles, so that it was impossible to know where sky ended and land began.

The emptiness and the lack of visual clues for comparisons of size or shape magnified any object several times. A single small rock, appearing huge, emphasized the empty flatness all around. A large tree on the far shore of a mirage evaporated as we approached into a stunted shrub a foot or two high. An object of uncertain shape appeared on the horizon apparently several miles away and I drove in its direction to find a lump of stone no more than nine inches across. Something about the regular shape caught my eye, and I stopped. The hard shiny rock had been hollowed out on top: it was a neolithic grain mortar, which must have been lying in this position in the *reg* for several thousand years, a striking witness to the timelessness of the desert. I left it in place, in the hope it would remain there for a few years more, before being collected for some dusty museum.

An owl had evidently used the grain mortar as a perch, because there were pellets of insect remains and small rodent teeth lying on it. It was difficult to believe that much could survive in such a place, where the chances for life seemed to be reduced to a minimum. There were almost no plants, no shelter from the sun or wind, and no food.

But as we drove on, a small party of Lichtenstein's sandgrouse moved on the ground ahead. These birds, like mottled sand-coloured pigeons, live in the open desert, but must drink every day, so are never more than 50 miles from a well or oasis. They fly in noisy flocks to water in the morning or evening, and this particular species will fly down quite deep well shafts, a small flock entering all together, like bats in a cave. The sandgrouse were alert at the approach of the Land Rover, and had their heads up, watching suspiciously. We stopped for a moment to look at them, but caution got the better of them and as if responding to a hidden signal they all rose at once, flying fast and low in formation over the *reg*, whistling excitedly. They must have been at the limit of their range from the last wells of Silet.

We drove in the heat all afternoon, and the sandgrouse were the last sign of life we saw that day. There were no more animals, no tracks, no plants. The last of the low conical hills, with a trace of silvery-blue rock down one side, had disappeared. All around mirages danced, but they had nothing to reflect but the pebbles of the *reg*. The gravel changed colour beneath the wheels of the car, turning black, white or grey. Once the surface was a hard yellowish sand; another time, blue and green pebbles. But everywhere it was flat and even, stretching away in front of us, behind and to each side, the sky always joining the land indistinctly along the same distant line ahead. There were no geographical positions in this infinite space, no individual co-ordinates. However fast we moved, nothing around us changed. Everywhere the distant horizon fell away to nothingness.

We stopped from time to time. When the engine was switched off my ears buzzed for a moment with its remembered noise, then there was

A large granite boulder, delicately poised as a result of centuries of erosion, marks the edge of the Tanezrouft reg, or gravel plain.

silence. It was not only that there was no noise; there was nothing to make any noise except the wind, and when that dropped, the silence was absolute. Such silence is so rare an experience that at first I felt almost a sense of foreboding, the sort that comes in a forest when the birds and animals fall silent at the approach of an intruder. But we were the only intruders and there were no animals to scare.

Time seemed no more real here than distance or space. Nothing had happened since the landscape was formed, thousands or millions of years before. In the Sahara's wet periods, perhaps a little grass grew and gazelle or antelope ventured out into the reg. But when it got drier again the grass and the animals disappeared. Now years and centuries go by and nothing changes. There is no reason why it should. Nothing happens here any more. Every day is like every other. If you have food and water and no appointments to keep you can move around in the reg for days without noticing them go by. You travel a hundred miles and make your camp on a patch of gravel identical to the one you left the day before. At dusk you do not look for a good place to stop; you simply turn off the engine and let the car coast to a halt, and that place will be no better and no worse than any other for a hundred thousand square miles around.

But time and space, apparently so irrelevant when all is going well, can turn against you. If you get lost, break down, or find a well dry, your situation suddenly changes. Distance is against you, the distance you can walk for help, the radius within which you can hope to find a well or people; and in the end time will get you too, the time you can survive on the water you have left, the time you can withstand the wind and sun.

The sun was sinking, losing its intense white glow. As it touched the horizon, it seemed to gather speed and size, so that after a slow descent down half the sky it suddenly became a huge flat orange disc and fell with unlikely speed into the distant reg, leaving only a purplish glow above the horizon. To the south, there were dark grey clouds against the washed blue sky. The gravel plain in front of us darkened and the details disappeared. The sky remained pale for another 20 minutes or so. Then darkness began to gain the whole landscape, and the air was suddenly cool. We stopped, made our camp and lit a fire. The terrifying dimensions of the reg were at once reduced to a human scale: a pool of light in the darkness, a carpet, supper things and beds close to the fire. Atitel sat with his blanket round his shoulders and baked an unleavened loaf for supper. He mixed millet flour and water to form a paste, then cleared a space in the centre of the embers and poured the mixture into a hollow in the hot sand. He covered the flat loaf with ash and glowing embers until it had cooked on top, and then turned it over to cook on the other side. When both sides were cooked, he brushed the ashes off, broke the loaf into pieces and dipped them into liquid butter. By the time we had eaten, it was bitterly cold. Zipped into my sleeping bag, I wrote the day's notes, and then lay back and watched the stars.

A strong north-east wind was blowing when I woke, and the air was full of dust. I wrapped my burnous round me, and struggled to make coffee on a gas burner, crouching to make a wind-shield with the cloak. Dust formed a thick layer on top of the coffee. When I started to load the Land Rover, the wind caught the burnous and billowed it out like a sail.

The horizon, yesterday so distant, had closed in to a few hundred yards of swirling dust. We were now without points of reference. We had gone to the north of the area that Atitel knew from caravans, and in any case, because of the speed of the Land Rover, he was not sure about the distance we had covered. When nomads travel with camels, distance is measured in time more than space—a day's journey with a good riding camel, two days' with laden baggage animals. Even in the featureless *reg*, a caravanner would know his rough position each night. (The nomads have a good memory for places they have seen before, but no supernatural navigational skills. There is, however, a tradition of blind guides in the Sahara, men who could check their position at the end of each day by the smell of the sand. Maurice Cortier, the French army officer who in 1912 was the first European to cross the western Tanez-rouft, was guided by a half-blind nomad.)

Out in the open *reg* it was easy to understand the importance and fascination of the science of navigation, and the role it played in exploration. Without landmarks we would have to use compasses. I had fitted an aircraft compass in the cab of the Land Rover, but it was not always accurate since the amount of metal around it—jerrycans and old ammunition boxes in which most of my kit was packed—interfered severely with its magnetic field. Every week or so it was necessary to adjust the correcting magnets to take account of the interference, and it was then accurate to within a degree or two on most readings, which was sufficient for everyday use. By recording on the Land Rover's milometer the distance travelled on each compass bearing it was possible to work out an approximate dead reckoning position each evening.

But something more accurate was needed now, and for this reason I had also brought an old army sun compass. Designed originally by Ralph Bagnold for his Libyan explorations, sun compasses were manu-

At close range, the apparently uniform surface of the reg displays an unexpected variety of colour and texture. In addition to gravel deposited by ancient floods, there are armoured surfaces made of rock fragments that have been laid bare as wind and rain eroded away loose soil, or have worked up from below ground as they expanded and contracted by day and night. On the surface, the fragments were split or darkened by weathering and smoothed by wind-blown sand.

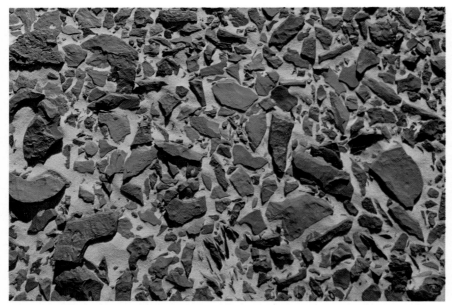

SILICA-HARDENED SANDSTONE

SANDSTONE WITH A DARK IRON-RICH COATING

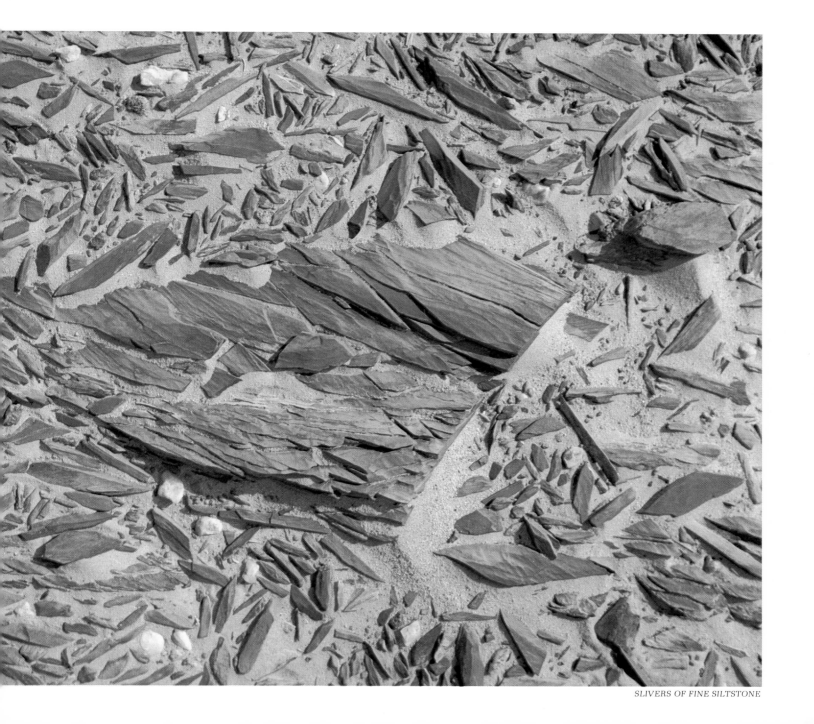

SLIVERS OF FINE SILTSTONE

factured for the British Army in North Africa in World War II, and can still be found at navigational instrument specialists. The principle is very simple. The instrument is the opposite of a sundial. With a sundial, if you know the position of north, you can tell the time. With a sun compass, if you know the time, you can tell the position of north. It is a beautifully designed brass disc with a vertical pin—or gnomon—in the middle. The course is set on the compass at the start of the day's run and the vehicle is driven so that the shadow of the gnomon is kept at that position. Since the compass has to be adjusted every quarter of an hour to correct for the sun's movements, I had mounted mine on the bonnet of the Land Rover where I could reach it without stopping.

I had worked out our previous evening's position by dead reckoning, and now calculated a course that would take us down towards Timmissao. The sun had risen, a faded white disc in the dust. It would hardly be casting a shadow yet, and we would have to rely on the magnetic compass for the moment. We set off with a low carpet of dust sweeping around the Land Rover's wheels.

We drove all morning and saw nothing. Towards midday the heat haze turned the clouds of dust into a shimmering fog. Atitel and I were both short-tempered from the wind and heat. We had trouble with the exhaust of the Land Rover, which had been badly knocked on a boulder in the Ahaggar and now finally came off. This was not serious, but I had to get down under the vehicle to mend it, wrapping a Tuareg veil round my head to keep out the heat and the dust. When the job was finished I drank from one of the *guerbas*. The water was evaporating fast, I noticed. We would have to be careful.

In good conditions, during the winter for example, people need quite small amounts of water. Théodore Monod, travelling in Mauritania, calculated on drinking two pints a day, all in tea, and using up to four pints for cooking rice. Being as frugal as this, it is possible to carry enough water by camel to have five weeks' autonomy from wells. Since no wells in the Sahara are as much as five weeks apart, this is more than enough for any exploration if you do not get lost. In a Land Rover or truck, of course, you can carry a lot more water.

But in the extreme heat, the human body can sweat up to 24 pints a day, and it has none of the versatility of camels and other desert animals towards water shortage. By the time it has lost about ten per cent of its weight, death is inevitable. It is not a pleasant way to die. The blood plasma is reduced and the blood becomes viscous. Circulation slows and body heat cannot be dissipated; an explosive heat rise leads to death.

The possibility of death from thirst is an inescapable part of the fabric of a desert nomad's life. A man alone, looking for a wandering camel, gets lost, and his body is found only months later. Sometimes the tragedy is on a large scale. In 1805 an entire salt caravan of 2,000 men and 1,800 camels died of thirst between Timbuktu and Taoudenni. In 1912, Maurice Cortier, crossing the Tanezrouft, found dozens of mummified bodies from a caravan that had tried to take a short cut three years earlier. "Dying of thirst, Arabs and black slaves had huddled together waiting for the help which never came," the French explorer wrote; "they died there, their eyes turned towards the mountains of the Ahnet, already visible on the horizon, where they knew that 50 kilometres away was the water that would save them; but they did not have the strength to make the final effort."

In the afternoon the wind dropped a little and the haze lifted. We continued across a landscape that remained flat and featureless, but towards evening I saw some whitened branches from a *had* bush blowing listlessly across the *reg*, the first sign of something living I had seen in 24 hours. Later that night we made our camp and lit a small fire with the remaining wood. Atitel produced a dry powder of millet, dates and onions and added water to make a thick white soup for supper.

As we drank the soup, I asked Atitel what the desert meant to him, and whether he would like to live elsewhere. He did not reply directly, but after a moment's thought told me about some of the times he had been out of the desert, to caravan towns like Timbuktu and Agades. The noise and the bustle of people were unpleasant and he was always happy to leave them; but he admitted it would be nice to be near a doctor when his children were ill. Then he asked about towns in Europe and whether it was true as he had heard that everyone had cars, not just rich merchants. He asked why I came here to the desert.

It was difficult to give him a straightforward reply. The Sahara meant many things to me, and the value of all of them lay in the contrast between the desert and town life in industrial Europe. Without this reference, Atitel could hardly be expected to understand my feelings. I tried to explain that I thought the Sahara was one of the last areas of the world where human influence was unobtrusive, and that this had important lessons for people who no longer lived close to nature, lessons not only about nature but also human nature. But I could see I was making little sense to him, and I was left to think about the answer myself.

The desert makes possible an intuitive understanding of two great, ungraspable notions: geological time and astronomical space. The forces by which the desert landscape was made are displayed openly and are repeated on a small scale each time a wadi flows. Before coming to the Sahara I had never had the feeling that a landscape evolves, like an organism almost; the slow pace of change now makes it possible to realize how long these forces have been at work. Likewise, when you sleep out night after night under the stars, watching the familiar constellations turn slowly and predictably above, space becomes a little less mysterious. One evening, lying on my back and looking at the night sky through binoculars, I saw the moons of Jupiter for the first time. The familiarity of another world with satellites gave me a shock of delight.

Surrounded by such a feeling of time and space, it is difficult to take the more extreme pretensions of the human race too seriously. Out in the Tanezrouft, we were no larger than fleas on a parade ground. Man here is more nearly on a level with the animals than elsewhere, part of an interlocking ecological network, facing the same extremes and uncertainties and requiring the same qualities; opportunism and persistence have survival value for an acacia, an addax or a human being. A grass seed that waits in the sand of a wadi bed for ten years, and then germinates, grows and flowers in a few days after rain has a lesson to teach. Gazelles, gerbils and snakes live beyond the bounds of the world normally inhabitable by people, and it is no bad thing to be reminded of man's ecological limitations, his lack of importance in the sweep of time and space, and his marginal importance among many of the biological destinies being worked out. You learn that all life—not just man— is precious. This lesson in humility is a good corrective to the arrogance of technological society.

People who live in the desert—nomads and those who come as travellers from outside—regain faculties easily lost elsewhere. The senses are sharpened. I heard better in the silence, could smell more acutely once away from diesel fuel and smoking chimneys. I knew the taste of water from different wells and lived by natural time, eating when I was hungry and sleeping when I was tired, rather than when the clock reached a certain point.

The desert is also a useful mirror for human nature. You live publicly there and your companions are always with you. News and opinion travel far and fast and there is no possibility of the reserved anonymity you can find in cities. You have to get on with small groups of people for long periods, in difficult conditions. Self reliance is an important virtue, challenge and danger are commonplace. Value is put on endurance,

Lifeless and swept almost bare of sand, the pebbled surface of the Tanezrouft reg stretches without interruption to the distant horizon.

adaptability, open-mindedness. And often you have to come to terms with great solitude, and learn to be alone. The desert teaches a certain hardness and strength; you learn to treat minor physical and psychological wounds with silence and scorn.

I found also, to my surprise, how little I needed. Making do with very little is one of the necessary skills of Saharan life, and moderation is the great nomad virtue: moderation in needs and wants, in gestures and talk, towards food and water. I learned how to make a neat and effective fire with little wood, how to wash in an inch of muddy water at the bottom of a bucket. Above all desert life teaches moderation in expectations; you hope and work for the best, but plan for the worst, and are not cast down when it happens. The reward is personal freedom and self-discipline in equal proportions.

The wind fell during the night and we woke the following morning to a clear sky. We cleared the camp site and tried to leave as evidence of our passage no more than trampled gravel and the white ash from our fire which would blow away in the next wind. I set a compass course calculated to bring us to Timmissao in the afternoon, and we set off.

The *reg* was the same faded greyish black colour, and the horizon the same flat line surrounding us unapproachably far away. Whenever we stopped to look for tracks or to examine the pebbles, we were wrapped in a cocoon of silence. This place seemed lifeless, our passage through it the main biological event for hundreds, perhaps thousands of years. Although there were probably bacteria and fungi spores in the sand and gravel, any larger plant or animal would only come here by accident, and would surely die.

It was easy to imagine that after a little more time in this empty landscape I would start having hallucinations, like the lone yachtsmen who see elephants or cars in the middle of the ocean. Such hallucinations are thought to be due to extreme sensory deprivation, and there can be few places on land where there is less distraction of the senses than in the *reg*. Indeed I found after our brief stops that I kept thinking we had left somebody behind, and the idea that there was another person with us continued to stick in the back of my mind as long as we were in the Tanezrouft.

But although the landscape did not alter, it was never monotonous. As the sun rose the light changed, and each hour brought a new overlay of colours on the gravel. In the early morning the primary colours of the *reg*, which were greyish-black with occasional patches of white, green, maroon or even blue, stretched fresh and clear towards the horizon. The sky was the palest of blues, with a furrow of white clouds high above. Later in the morning as the sun rose higher, the horizon became indistinct, and the reg dissolved in a haze that shimmered like a pool ruffled by a light breeze; all colours were muted by the heat and the penetrating white glare of the sun.

Towards midday a Painted Lady butterfly zig-zagged across our path. The sight of something living after two days of empty reg was an event, a rumour of change in this apparently changeless landscape. And not long afterwards the level horizon was broken for the first time since we had set off by an indistinct shape that grew slowly into a line of sand dunes. I drove round them warily, unused to any surface but the hard gravel of the reg. Beyond was a long straight line of trees which ended in a large dark shape, like an avenue of chestnuts leading to a stately house. But as we approached, the chestnuts turned into tattered acacias, the avenue was the line of a tiny wadi, and the stately house no more than a block of sandstone. Beyond it were other blocks, building up to a low cliff that stretched obliquely away from us. This was the place called Timmissao, and the well we were searching for was somewhere at its foot.

We stopped to take in this sudden show of vertical lines. In the sandy ground there were scattered bushes of had, the spiky gunmetal-blue plant loved by camels. They were small and compact for protection against the wind. I found a black and white feather lodged in one bush, which suggested that a white-crowned black wheatear was somewhere about, and sure enough a young bird turned up after a few minutes. It was extremely tame, with nothing whatever to fear here, and perched on the Land Rover to get a better look at us.

In the afternoon we followed the cliff, and as the light was fading saw the twin rock towers that marked the entrance to the canyon of Timmissao itself. A nearly full moon had risen and lit our way down the canyon, the sand silvery yellow in the moonlight, and the rocks dark with inky black shadows marking crevices and hollows. We stopped just beyond the well, and made camp on a patch of clean sand up against the rock wall of the canyon. There were large bushes of flowers conspicuous against the pale moonlit sky, and a bat swooped low over us as we ate supper on my carpet. A huge solifugid camel-spider raced past waving its palps, and a black beetle trundled over the sand, disturbed by the noise we were making. For animals alert to the slightest vibrations in the sand our arrival must have been like an earthquake. We were tired and dusty, but we had returned to the land of the living.

I felt as though I had reached Zerzura, the legendary oasis that lured explorers to the Libyan Desert in the 1920s and 1930s. Zerzura has never been found and it has come to symbolize an ideal in desert exploration, the unattainable that lies just beyond the horizon. And that evening at Timmissao I felt that I had reached some sort of ideal place, so isolated that it was a baseline from which the rest of the world could be measured.

I tried to explain to Atitel how I felt. Seen from Timmissao, the disadvantages and advantages of the urban civilization from which I had come were obvious, and there were—for me at least—important lessons to be learned from this confrontation of landscapes and lifestyles. The first was that the Sahara reaffirms the natural context of man. People tend to think of nature in terms of its immediate use to man, and the desert in particular seems to be of little use. Now I had begun to see the Sahara as it really is, a unique, evolving biological unit, with highly adapted plants and animals, and specialized human societies; and its value as a reservoir of biological potential and genetic inheritance, though intangible, was real. It was salutary, also, to be reminded of the essential lifelines leading back to nature from even the most sophisticated urban communities. In the desert I drew all my drinking water from wells. It was hard work, and the water was often dirty; I doubted that I should ever take taps and clean city water for granted again.

In the same way the Sahara reaffirms the historical context of man. The grain mortar we had seen was evidence of the transience of human occupation. Here at Timmissao there seemed no reason why technological civilization should not go the same way as the neolithic one. Nothing very much would change in the Tanezrouft if it did.

Here, also, the idea that unlimited increases in the production and consumption of material goods were equivalent to increasing human happiness did not hold up. Atitel had many fewer goods than I had, but was not noticeably unhappy about it. I myself was living in the desert much more frugally than at home, and was enjoying it. Moreover, scarcity of material things was more than compensated by other, immaterial, gains: humour, courage and endurance, trust in my companions, time to observe the behaviour of butterflies, a good night's sleep under the stars. Such things provide a more secure base for the good life since they are not manufactured from scarce resources nor, like possessions, can they be appropriated by the rich and powerful.

But how valid were these conclusions to Atitel? It was all very well for a person from a rich industrial society to rediscover important truths about himself and the society he came from by means of a voyage in the desert, but the nomads who lived here might have different ideas. I was not ready to forget that my children probably had twice as much chance of surviving to become adults as did Atitel's, precisely because of the urban civilization I was now judging so harshly. Until the Sahara's huge riches of oil, uranium, iron and copper had been exploited, until Atitel had a material standard of living that was not grossly different from mine, it was impossible for me to urge on him the advantages of the wilderness. These developments, together with the drought in the south, might even destroy his society. But the choice between civilization and wilderness was his alone. Even if, as I strongly believed, there were some universal truths to be discovered about the relationship between man, society and nature in such a place, clearly each person had to discover them for himself. Happily, I thought to myself, Atitel and I seemed to share much the same views, and I was hopeful about the future.

In the morning there was no wind, and the sky was clear. For a day, we explored Timmissao. The crevices of the low sandstone cliffs were scattered with flowering plants and green trees. In one of them a pair of willow warblers was searching briskly for food; they showed no sign of exhaustion after their voyage from Europe across the Mediterranean and most of the Sahara. Perhaps they were filling up for the last part of the desert crossing, or maybe they had decided to spend the winter here. There were tracks in the sand of lizards and beetles, and a line of sandgrouse flew over my head towards the well. Seeing me they circled back and disappeared above the rock. When I approached the well, four rock pigeons flew out; they had been drinking at the bottom, about 15 feet down.

In the afternoon, I set a course on the sun compass to take us directly to Silet, and we started back across the Tanezrouft. In a short time we were alone again in the gravel plain with the horizon stretching limitlessly all around us.

A Gallery of Desert Sculpture

Under the immensity of the desert sky, bare rock and flowing sands can form landscapes of stark and alien simplicity—"uncompromising landscapes", in the words of Jon Gardey who took most of these pictures, "that have had all feeling, all tenderness, all humanity eroded away."

Yet "the silent, fire-cleansed emptiness" is also strikingly—almost artificially—beautiful, and even before Gardey saw the results of his work, he looked on the desert in artistic terms. "The Sahara was a gallery, limited only by the vast hemisphere of blue overhead and the needle-etched line of the horizon, so distant as to be unreachable. Into this gallery were put sculptures of erosion. Sometimes they filled it with their shapes and dominated it. At other times, they were servants of the space, squeezed by the blue sky and yellow sand. Towers of rock became mere punctuation marks above their own shadows."

The desert itself seemed to Gardey to be a marriage of science and art. "The grains of sand had tumbled to the foot of the dunes," he says, "according to strict laws of gravity. The line of the dune crest was an aerodynamic curve, one that could also have represented the solution to an equation in calculus. The laws of nature had produced in the rocks and sand an art that was both natural and abstract. It was a combination of the real and the surreal— mysterious, subtly disturbing, with a dream-like serenity or an atmosphere of undefined menace."

Such unsettling effects are mostly produced by the light. "At midday," Gardey found, "the desert was flooded with a pure sunlight not seen in the temperate zones, white light of such power that it reduced the forms to insignificance by removing their shadows. The light burnt the colour out of the landscape, leaving it sterile and helpless.

"Later, as the sun approached the horizon, the forms rose and prevailed finally black and sharp, etched against the orange-yellow of the sky, a new light that for an hour at sunset provided relief from the harshness of the day."

Gardey felt that this same light, present since before the desert-gallery was created, drew him back into the far distant past, "to the very beginning of time before the lightning flashed and the first rains fell to produce life on earth." His wanderings in this pure, primal landscape seemed "a violation" of natural laws.

A STUDY OF GRAVEL, ROCKS, SAND AND SKY IN ALGERIA

A ROCK COLUMN SUNK IN THE STIPPLED SAND

GRASSY TUFTS IN A DALI-ESQUE DUNESCAPE

SUN-HALOED TOTEMS OF SANDBLASTED STONE

SCULPTED ROCK FINGERS AGAINST A METALLIC SKY

A MOUND ERUPTING FROM THE ADMER ERG

Bibliography

Bagnold, Ralph A., *Libyan Sands—Travel in a Dead World*. Hodder and Stoughton, 1935.

Bagnold, Ralph A., *The Physics of Blown Sand and Desert Dunes*. Chapman Hall Ltd., 1971.

Barth, Heinrich, *Travels and Discoveries in North and Central Africa* (5 vols). Longman, Brown, Green, Longmans, and Roberts, 1857-58.

Bernus, E. and S., *Du Sel et des Dattes*. Centre Nigerien de Recherches Scientifiques, 1972.

Boahon, A. Adu, *Britain, the Sahara and the Western Sudan 1788-1861*. Clarendon, 1964.

Bovill, E. W., *The Golden Trade of the Moors*, 2nd ed. Oxford University Press, 1968.

Briggs, L. Cabot, *The Living Races of the Sahara Desert*. Peabody Museum, 1958.

Brown, Robert, *Africa and its Explorers*, Vol. I. Cassell and Co. Ltd., 1892.

Caillé, R., *Travels through Central Africa to Timbuctoo and across the Great Desert to Morocco, performed in the years 1824-28* (2 vols.). Henry Colburn and Richard Bentley, 1830.

Capot-Rey, R., *Le Sahara Français*. Presses Universitaires de France, 1953.

Cloudsley-Thompson, J. L. and Chadwick, M. J., *Life in Deserts*. Foulis, 1964.

Cooke, R. U. and Warren, Andrew, *Geomorphology in Deserts*. Batsford, 1973.

Cortier, Maurice, *D'une Rive à l'Autre du Sahara*. Larose, 1908.

Dekeyser, P. L. and Derivot, J., *La Vie Animale au Sahara*. Colin, 1959.

Denham, D. and Clapperton, H., *Narrative of Travels and Discoveries in Northern and Central Africa in the Years 1822, 1823, 1824*. John Murray, 1826.

Diégo, Charles, *Sahara*. Editions du Moghreb, 1935.

Dubief, J., *Le Climat du Sahara* (2 vols). Institut de Recherches Sahariennes, 1959-63.

Duveyrier, H., *Les Touareg du Nord*. Challamel, 1864.

Etchécopar, R. D. and Hüe, François, *The Birds of North Africa*. Oliver and Boyd, 1967.

Gardner, Brian, *The Quest for Timbuctoo*. Cassell, 1968.

Gast, M., *Alimentation des Populations de l'Ahaggar*. Arts et Métiers Graphiques, 1968.

Gillet, H., "L'Oryx algazelle et l'Addax au Tchad." *La Terre et la Vie*, vol. 3 (1965), pp. 257-272.

Gautier, E. F., *Le Sahara*. Payot, 1928.

Hall, D. N., "A Simple Method of Navigating in Deserts." *Geographic Journal*, vol. 133 (1967), pp. 192-205.

Heim de Balsac, H., "Biogéographie des Mammifères et Oiseaux de l'Afrique du Nord." *Bulletin Biologique Française et Belgique-Supplément*, vol. 21 (1936).

Jacques-Meunié, D., *Cités Anciennes de Mauritanie*. Klincksieck, 1961.

Kingston, William H. G., *Travels of Park, Denham and Clapperton*. Routledge, 1886.

Kruger, C., *Sahara*. Putnams, 1969.

Lhote, H., *Les Touaregs du Hoggar*. 2nd ed. Payot, 1955.

Lhote, H., *The Search for the Tassili Frescoes*. Hutchinson, 1959.

Mauny, R., *Gravures, Peintures et Inscriptions Rupestres de l'Ouest Africain*. Institut Français de l'Afrique Noire, 1954.

Mauny, R., *Tableau Géographique de l'Ouest Africain au Moyen Age*. Institut Français de l'Afrique Noire, 1961.

Monod, Théodore, *Méharées—Explorations au Vrai Sahara*. Editions Je Sers, 1937.

Monod, Théodore, *Majabat al-Koubra—Contribution à l'Etude de l'Empty Quarter Ouest-Saharien*. Institut Français de l'Afrique Noire, 1958.

Monod, Théodore, "The Late Tertiary and Pleistocene in the Sahara" in *African Ecology and Human Evolution*. Eds C. Howell and F. Bourlière. Methuen, 1964.

Monod, Théodore, *Les Déserts*. Horizons de France, 1973.

Moorhouse, Geoffrey, *The Fearful Void*. Hodder and Stoughton, 1974.

Moreau, R. E., "Problems of Mediterranean-Saharan Migration." *Ibis*, vol. 103a (1961), pp. 373-427, 580-623.

Moreau, R. E., *The Palaearctic-African Bird Migration Systems*. Academic Press, 1972.

Nicolaisen, J., *Ecology and Culture of the Pastoral Tuareg*. National Museum of Copenhagen, 1963.

Norris, H. T., *Saharan Myth and Saga*. Clarendon, 1972.

Quézel, P., *La Végétation du Sahara*. Masson, 1965.

Richardson, J., *Travels in the Great Desert of Sahara in 1845-6* (2 vols). Bentley, 1848.

Schiffers, H., *Die Sahara und Ihre Randgebiete* (3 vols). München Weltforum Verlag, 1971-73.

Schmidt-Nielsen, K., *Desert Animals. Physiological Problems of Heat and Water*. Oxford University Press, 1964.

Swift, Jeremy, "Tuareg of the Sahara Desert" in *Peoples of the Earth*, vol. 17, *The Arab World*. Ed. Ahmed Al-Shahi. Danbury, 1973.

Tricart, J., *Le Modelé des Régions Sèches*. Société d'Etudes pour le Développement Economique et Sociale, 1969.

UNESCO, *Nomades et Nomadisme au Sahara*, 1963.

Wellard, J., *The Great Sahara*. Hutchinson of London, 1964.

Acknowledgements

The author and editors wish to thank the following: Algerian Government Tourist Office: Michel Anna, Chad; Ibn Battuta, Tangiers; Martin Brendell, London; Patrick Carter, Cambridge; Jean Djigui Keita, Bamako; Sally Foy, London; Mbery ag Rhissa, Goundam; Russell Miller, London; Professor Théodore Monod, Paris; Charles Nairn, London; Lady Oxmantown, Teheran; Marianne Rupp, Bamako; Mamadou Sarr, Bamako; Sidati ag Cheik, Aguelhoc; Susan Stafford, Taklit.

Picture Credits

Index

Numerals in italics indicate a photograph or drawing of the subject mentioned.

Colour reproduction by
Printing Developments International Ltd.,
Leeds, England—a Time Inc. subsidiary.
Filmsetting by C. E. Dawkins (Typesetters) Ltd., London, SE1 1UN.
Smeets Lithographers, Weert. Printed in Holland.
Bound by Proost en Brandt N.V., Amsterdam.